A NEW GENERAL ARITHMETIC — PART A

Note:

A NEW GENERAL ARITHMETIC — PART B   (ISBN 0 85950 130 2)
is a necessary companion to this volume.

ANSWERS TO A NEW GENERAL ARITHMETIC — PARTS A and B   (ISBN 0 85950 132 9)
are available to teachers.

Also available:

A NEW GENERAL ARITHMETIC — COMPLETE EDITION   (ISBN 0 85950 131 0)
containing both Parts A and B together with Answers

The publishers will be pleased to supply further information about this series, or other books from the same author on request. A full list of Stanley Thornes (Publishers) mathematics titles is also available.

A NEW GENERAL ARITHMETIC

PART A

Ewart Smith MSc

Head of Mathematics Department
Tredegar Comprehensive School

Stanley Thornes (Publishers) Ltd

First published in 1983 by

Stanley Thornes (Publishers) Ltd
Educa House
Old Station Drive
Leckhampton
CHELTENHAM GL53 0DN

Reprinted 1984 with minor corrections

British Library Cataloguing in Publication Data

Smith, Ewart
  A new general arithmetic.
  Pt. A
  1. Arithmetic—1961—
  I. Title
  513   QA107

  ISBN 0-85950-112-4

Typeset by Tech-Set, Gateshead, Tyne & Wear.
Printed and bound in Great Britain at The Pitman Press, Bath.

CONTENTS

PART B

PREFACE

This two-part book offers a complete course in General Arithmetic covering all the topics examined at CSE and 'O' level by the various examining boards. It may also be used by students following RSA, BEC and TEC courses, as well as those hoping to obtain certificates of proficiency in arithmetic including the new AEB examinations in Basic Arithmetic and Proficiency in Arithmetic.

A comprehensive range of examples is offered, supported by a simple down-to-earth text which includes several hundred worked examples. The number and range of difficulty of the exercises is such that, while there is sufficient to keep the weaker student fully occupied, there are also numerous questions which the best of students will find demanding.

The book is presented in two parts:

Part A covers the basic arithmetic normally studied during the first three years in the secondary school, which inevitably requires reinforcement in the fourth and subsequent years.

Part B is mainly concerned with civic and social arithmetic. While some of the topics are frequently introduced in the third year, its primary aim is to satisfy fourth and fifth-year students, as well as those 16 + students who, in various educational establishments, are aiming to make their knowledge of the subject as complete as possible.

Revision papers are given at regular intervals and a chapter is included specifically dealing with imperial units, since these are still required by many industries and certain examining bodies.

Another aim of the book is to provide a reservoir of examples at all levels, which I hope will enable readers to become better informed and more useful citizens.

Many of those who use this book will be the proud owners of electronic calculators. Provided the examination rules allow it, their use should be encouraged, for I believe that they will open a new door to the many students who previously became bogged down in the mechanics of the four rules when any numbers other than the simplest occurred.

It should be realised that the use of a calculator places an even greater emphasis on estimation and approximation and, therefore, on the understanding of basic arithmetic.

I would like to thank my former colleague, Mr Tom Thomas, for all the hard work he has put in checking through the answers, as well as Mr John Roberts, MA, and Mr Wyn Davies, BA, for the kind suggestions they made after reading the typescript. Finally I am indebted to the following examining boards for permission to use their questions:

Associated Examining Board (AEB)
Joint Matriculation Board (JMB)
Oxford and Cambridge Schools Examination Board (O & C)
Southern Universities Joint Board (SU)
Welsh Joint Education Committee (WJEC)

Ewart Smith
1983

PART
A

1

WHOLE NUMBERS

EXERCISE 1   NUMBERS IN WORDS AND FIGURES

Write the following numbers in figures:

1. Three thousand and twenty-seven
2. Five thousand one hundred and seventy-six
3. Nine thousand five hundred
4. Four thousand eight hundred and forty-two
5. Sixteen thousand and fifty
6. Twelve thousand eight hundred and seventy-two
7. One thousand seven hundred and eighty-three
8. Twenty-two thousand nine hundred
9. Four hundred thousand
10. One hundred and ten thousand
11. Eighteen thousand and forty
12. Four thousand and three
13. Thirteen hundred thousand
14. Eight thousand six hundred and thirty
15. One hundred thousand and seventy-two
16. Seven thousand and eighty-seven
17. Forty-seven thousand eight hundred and sixty-five
18. Five hundred and fifty thousand seven hundred
19. Two million five hundred thousand
20. Thirteen million five hundred and seventy-two.

Write the following numbers in words:

21. 426	**22.** 927	**23.** 126	**24.** 430
25. 655	**26.** 926	**27.** 1500	**28.** 3750
29. 82 000	**30.** 67 500	**31.** 347 005	**32.** 592 070
33. 142 560	**34.** 872 660	**35.** 394 000	**36.** 462 500
37. 500 873	**38.** 892 660	**39.** 1 270 000	

40. 3 050 047.

EXERCISE 2   ADDITION

1. 34 43	**2.** 62 15	**3.** 47 51	**4.** 71 18
5. 45 53	**6.** 27 43	**7.** 35 55	**8.** 52 38
9. 44 36	**10.** 29 41	**11.** 16 25	**12.** 27 44
13. 65 29	**14.** 56 35	**15.** 47 39	**16.** 27 83
17. 49 57	**18.** 63 79	**19.** 48 56	**20.** 33 88
21. 31 214 512	**22.** 22 703 154	**23.** 315 42 420	**24.** 155 510 23
25. 430 521 47	**26.** 134 212 431	**27.** 514 142 223	**28.** 641 233 113
29. 270 309 120	**30.** 105 482 312	**31.** 127 314 124	**32.** 315 414 123

33.	516 214 233 ——	34.	142 326 534 ——	35.	138 128 714 ——	36.	731 148 170 ——
37.	233 581 174 ——	38.	282 351 366 ——	39.	114 238 429 ——	40.	331 269 307 ——
41.	921 342 625 ——	42.	711 822 353 ——	43.	931 223 444 ——	44.	731 823 925 ——
45.	622 651 716 ——	46.	374 255 165 ——	47.	516 434 915 ——	48.	372 149 165 ——
49.	527 443 849 ——	50.	748 627 324 ——	51.	493 614 728 ——	52.	592 115 638 ——
53.	421 537 654 ——	54.	792 535 292 ——	55.	817 443 593 ——	56.	463 592 137 ——
57.	926 321 743 ——	58.	517 728 395 ——	59.	826 430 994 ——	60.	621 126 632 ——
61.	24 317 9280 ——	62.	142 37 8034 ——	63.	5319 928 64 ——	64.	584 6741 93 ——
65.	8264 73 547 ——	66.	923 417 2934 ——	67.	6214 327 436 ——	68.	423 5911 732 ——

3

69. 2656
431
724
_____

70. 716
593
3714
_____

71. 9261
437
563
_____

72. 627
5219
856
_____

73. 736
391
6241
_____

74. 927
7814
338
_____

75. 8624
698
532
_____

76. 2064
5214
1828
_____

77. 5129
1427
2173
_____

78. 2174
3924
4315
_____

79. 3893
2636
1418
_____

80. 5624
3093
1174
_____

81. 5936
4285
7261
_____

82. 6923
5473
3364
_____

83. 9537
2143
6572
_____

84. 4079
5321
1505
_____

85. 7438
6537
1293
_____

86. 2420
263
5142
619
_____

87. 5390
537
829
7241
_____

88. 9281
4416
327
782
_____

89. 176
2439
7210
826
_____

90. 362
9211
655
3140
_____

91. 7241
3789
5253
742
_____

92. 2451
4157
3624
931
_____

93. 4319
526
3345
2785
_____

94. 9280
4265
371
5117
_____

95. 320
4217
5235
9629
_____

96. 4261
5372
3649
2143
_____

97. 5921
3726
2937
6273
_____

98. 7437
4126
3324
3324
_____

99. 1049
8216
5566
7243
_____

100. 9210
8571
2239
3591
_____

101. 47 321
52 164
39 207
15 367
_____

102. 65 784
56 225
13 567
30 057
_____

103. 46 357
83 465
43 678
67 448
_____

104. 22 533
77 345
56 920
36 378
_____

105.	106.	107.	108.
84 567	21 437	68 433	33 245
98 254	37 214	76 843	46 233
30 574	92 956	13 568	26 354
12 217	72 140	54 763	66 833
————	36 210	57 802	50 764
	————	————	————

109.	110.
22 647	85 572
12 997	53 882
84 562	43 378
45 267	99 837
77 880	56 600
————	————

111. 262 + 345 + 826

112. 592 + 437 + 127

113. 927 + 412 + 816

114. 347 + 727 + 839

115. 614 + 824 + 334

116. 539 + 224 + 739

117. 2436 + 413 + 7264

118. 5146 + 2475 + 9265

119. 1342 + 6149 + 7343

120. 2143 + 5114 + 8263

121. 9624 + 41 739 + 536

122. 724 + 4165 + 16 347

123. 11 434 + 2963 + 736

124. 32 692 + 515 + 8173

125. 36 424 + 59 364 + 1166

126. 8164 + 14 392 + 31 519

127. 87 419 + 23 550 + 51 962

128. 15 437 + 75 392 + 63 420

129. 32 711 + 59 267 + 22 624

130. 31 415 + 51 163 + 72 344

131. Find the sum of all the numbers from 1 to 20.

132. Find the sum of all the even numbers from 98 to 124.

133. Find the sum of all the odd numbers from 159 to 163.

134. Find the sum of all the whole numbers between 19 and 43 which are exactly divisible by 5.

135. In a local election Mrs Addicott receives 1264 votes, Mr Beanham 972 votes, Mrs Capstick 53 votes and Mr Dearnley 474 votes. How many people voted?

136. In a parliamentary election the votes cast were as follows: Miss Edwards 8492, Mrs Shorey 24 537, Mr Grafter 16 934 and Mr Gibson 4219. In addition there were 143 spoilt voting papers and 7246 registered voters failed to record their vote. Find the size of the total electorate.

137. During the first six months of the year the following numbers visited a zoo: 1649, 2434, 4621, 12 047, 27 267 and 35 937. Find the total number of visitors during the six month period.

138. Motorway exits along a certain section of the M4 are numbered 5 to 27. How many exits are there in that section?

139. Last year the number of vehicles each month failing to obtain an MOT certificate at Bryant's Vehicle Testing Station were as follows: 26, 13, 8, 15, 41, 12, 9, 17, 24, 19, 17, 24. Find the total number of failures for the year.

140. During the last week of January the number of new cars leaving a factory was: Monday 934, Tuesday 1026, Wednesday 1139, Thursday 1243 and Friday 976. How many cars left the factory during the week?

EXERCISE 3 SUBTRACTION

1.	57 42	2.	95 64	3.	47 36	4.	79 57
5.	68 25	6.	429 217	7.	538 307	8.	792 682
9.	645 531	10.	384 213	11.	82 64	12.	56 39
13.	42 37	14.	83 67	15.	73 27	16.	242 127
17.	638 309	18.	436 219	19.	584 156	20.	725 518
21.	572 284	22.	415 187	23.	633 268	24.	725 589
25.	814 276	26.	4462 3421	27.	3718 1407	28.	4231 3111
29.	5926 2615	30.	8756 3423	31.	5934 2155	32.	8261 3189

33.	9114	34.	3720	35.	6535	36.	3178
	1076		1077		3489		1689

37.	4629	38.	5198	39.	7266	40.	8431
	2733		1589		2378		4597

41.	73 400	42.	56 592	43.	14 634	44.	32 420
	24 387		39 447		11 894		15 555

45. 92 705
24 887

Subtract the second number from the first:

46. 5437, 2466   **47.** 8293, 1739

48. 4537, 934   **49.** 16 421, 8734

50. 24 214, 16 845.

Subtract the first number from the second:

51. 473, 5294   **52.** 892, 1004

53. 3412, 20 040   **54.** 15 721, 24 827

55. 3492, 10 477.

Simplify:

56. $526 + 137 + 293 - 756$ **57.** $743 - 93 - 47 - 236$

58. $127 + 539 - 464 - 98$ **59.** $35 + 242 - 63 - 129$

60. $1000 - 327 - 113 - 424$ **61.** $446 - 314 + 27 - 68$

62. $2000 - 573 - 78 - 498$

63. $5274 - 167 - 87 - 3421 - 245$

64. $1263 - 2114 + 1737 - 142 - 34$

65. $154 - 726 - 2241 + 3440.$

66. What number must be added to 1472 to give 5664?

67. What number must be added to 732 to give 1021?

68. What number must be added to 5637 to give 24 371?

69. What number must be added to 1249 to give 7374?

70. Subtract three hundred and thirty-four from seven hundred and ninety-seven.

71. Subtract two hundred and forty-nine from five hundred and fifty-six.

72. Subtract three hundred and fifty-seven from nine hundred and seventy-three.

73. Subtract four thousand three hundred and seventy-one from sixteen thousand.

74. Subtract five thousand five hundred and forty-seven from ten thousand.

75. Subtract nine thousand two hundred and sixty-four from twenty-nine thousand seven hundred and seventy-six.

76. The crowd at Old Trafford for a first division game on a particular Saturday was 45 427 but on the following Saturday 4937 fewer spectators turned up. What was the attendance for the second game?

77. On consecutive Saturdays the attendance at Portman Road was 35 472 and 32 789. Find the decrease in attendance.

78. In a large school there are 127 fewer pupils this year than last year, and it is expected that there will be a further fall of 88 pupils next year. If there are 1347 pupils in the school this year, calculate the number of pupils (a) in the school last year, (b) expected to be in the school next year.

79. In a school with 1395 pupils there are 47 more girls than boys. How many boys are there?

80. In a factory with a workforce consisting of 265 men, 569 women and 102 young people, 788 people are paid a weekly wage while the remainder receive an annual salary. How many are paid a salary?

EXERCISE 4   MULTIPLICATION

1.	34 × 5	2.	42 × 6	3.	29 × 7	4.	52 × 8
5.	72 × 4	6.	94 × 5	7.	78 × 3	8.	47 × 9
9.	242 × 5	10.	163 × 7	11.	521 × 4	12.	763 × 2
13.	372 × 7	14.	314 × 9	15.	824 × 6	16.	916 × 4
17.	615 × 3	18.	342 × 8	19.	241 × 7	20.	528 × 5
21.	154 × 20	22.	213 × 30	23.	621 × 40	24.	451 × 50
25.	759 × 60	26.	448 × 70	27.	139 × 80	28.	291 × 90
29.	49 × 53	30.	37 × 42	31.	14 × 53	32.	56 × 27
33.	67 × 32	34.	75 × 47	35.	53 × 16	36.	44 × 73

37. 98×56	38. 82×41	39. 57×24	40. 27×54
41. 87×21	42. 42×29	43. 63×51	44. 72×43
45. 65×98	46. 43×55	47. 73×32	48. 31×82
49. 13×19	50. 27×54	51. 73×32	52. 67×44
53. 73×83	54. 84×92	55. 96×97	56. 34×95
57. 220×21	58. 162×24	59 313×32	60. 415×33
61. 520×26	62. 724×42	63. 272×51	64. 413×46
65. 372×61	66. 518×72	67. 472×81	68. 754×84
69. 425×56	70. 671×44	71. 824×36	72. 339×27
73. 812×74	74. 641×56	75. 592×68	76. 392×85
77. 558×91	78. 637×94	79. 748×97	80. 829×96
81. 220×124	82. 720×222	83. 635×321	
84. 913×504	85. 421×312	86. 527×213	
87. 641×421	88. 513×632	89. 531×748	
90. 293×678	91. 913×543	92. 816×378	
93. 917×413	94. 921×173	95. 492×317	
96. 646×821	97. 636×325	98. 749×527	
99. 827×514	100. 752×926		

101. Multiply the sum of 42 and 93 by their difference.

102. Multiply the sum of 59 and 104 by their difference.

103. Multiply the sum of 72 and 237 by their difference.

104. Multiply the sum of 242 and 173 by their difference.

105. Multiply the sum of 372 and 843 by their difference.

106. On a particular day a supermarket sells 76 large packets of ginger biscuits, 47 medium packets and 82 small packets. If a large packet contains 36 biscuits, a medium packet 24 and a small packet 18, how many biscuits were sold on that day?

107. A bus company operates 27 fifty-seater buses, 14 forty-five-seater buses and 5 eighteen-seater buses. How many seats does the bus company have available?

108. At a concert 247 seats were sold at £7 each, 534 at £5 each and 413 at £3 each. Find the total amount of money taken.

109. A soccer player estimates that he runs 9 miles during a match. If he plays twice a week for a thirty-six week season, find the total distance he has run during the season's matches.

9

110. A bus from Franton to Highlow travels a distance of 28 miles each way. Each day, a bus starts from Franton at 7 a.m. and takes 4 hours for a round trip. It returns to Franton for the last time at 11 p.m. Find the total distance travelled by the bus in (a) a week, (b) a year.

EXERCISE 5 DIVISION

Divide:

1.	612 by 4	2.	1535 by 5
3.	1446 by 6	4.	5341 by 7
5.	336 by 8	6.	1575 by 9
7.	6545 by 11	8.	1176 by 12
9.	8112 by 13	10.	5936 by 14
11.	1397 by 11	12.	4644 by 9
13.	6258 by 21	14.	4064 by 16
15.	1258 by 17	16.	7536 by 24
17.	6020 by 35	18.	2277 by 33
19.	26 164 by 62	20.	12 528 by 54
21.	6888 by 84	22.	44 091 by 71
23.	19 928 by 47	24.	13 230 by 54
25.	98 332 by 124	26.	40 812 by 76
27.	28 213 by 89	28.	202 370 by 245
29.	53 573 by 317	30.	77 322 by 789.

Divide, giving quotient and remainder:

31.	436 by 9	32.	529 by 7
33.	613 by 8	34.	873 by 6
35.	447 by 8	36.	693 by 9
37.	443 by 11	38.	926 by 12
39.	734 by 14	40.	1429 by 16
41.	2936 by 17	42.	4453 by 13
43.	8264 by 19	44.	7436 by 24
45.	5916 by 18	46.	2426 by 54
47.	9264 by 63	48.	3373 by 42

49. 4246 by 37

50. 7369 by 49

51. 2537 by 82

52. 92 984 by 126

53. 71 564 by 361

54. 33 925 by 417

55. 11 424 by 314

56. 53 615 by 424

57. 49 937 by 636

58. 245 678 by 597

59. 89 345 by 852

60. 714 394 by 948.

61. Divide twenty-two thousand seven hundred and twenty-four by ninety-two.

62. Divide eighteen thousand seven hundred and forty-six by two hundred and thirty-two.

63. Divide two hundred and twenty-two thousand four hundred and forty by six hundred and sixty-four.

64. Divide ninety-one thousand two hundred and sixty-four by seven hundred and thirty-six.

65. Divide fifty-nine thousand five hundred and eight by one thousand and forty-four.

66. Divide the sum of 959 and 685 by their difference.

67. Divide the sum of 1455 and 873 by their difference.

68. Divide the product of 357 and 408 by their difference.

69. Divide the product of 64 and 35 by their sum.

70. Divide the product of 126 and 84 by their sum.

71. In a library a bookshelf will take 47 books. How many shelves are required for 4371 books?

72. Forty-nine-seater coaches are available to transport air passengers from the airport to the city centre. If 1255 passengers are to be transported, how many coaches will be required, and how many spare seats will there be on the last coach assuming that all the others are full?

73. My car burns 1 gallon of petrol for every 38 miles. How many gallons will be required for a journey of 608 miles?

74. There are 1428 pupils in a school with a teaching staff of 84. How many pupils is this for each teacher?

75. A cardboard carton will hold 72 tins of baked beans. How many cartons are required to pack 4680 tins of beans?

76. Cigars are packed in packets of 3. How many packets are required to pack 855 cigars?

77. A factory produces 3545 car wheels in a week. If each car requires 5 wheels, how many cars does this cater for?

78. The borough council allocates £7 627 000 for new houses. If each house is estimated to cost £14 500 to build, how many houses do they intend to build?

79. How many 2 kilogram packets of sugar may be filled from a 5 tonne delivery? (1 tonne = 1000 kilograms)

80. How many egg boxes, each of which will hold 6 eggs, are required to pack 1000 eggs? How many eggs are there in the last box?

81. If sound travels at 330 metres per second, how long will it take for a person 1980 metres away to hear a clap of thunder?

82. Lamp standards are placed at 50 metre intervals. If the last standard on a stretch of road is 2150 metres from the first, how many standards are there?

83. A mail order firm has £14 000 to spend on promoting a new product. If it costs 35p to send to each household, how many households will they be able to send to?

84. How many years, each with 365 days, are there in 16 425 days?

85. There are 321 516 voters in the county of Centreshire. For local elections the county is divided into regions, each region having 2748 voters. Into how many regions will the county be divided?

EXERCISE 6   MISCELLANEOUS EXAMPLES

1. A palette of building blocks consists of five layers each containing 27 blocks. How many palettes of blocks must be ordered if a particular building is expected to require 112 000 blocks?

2. There are 12 460 cans of peas in the stock room of a hypermarket. If 76 boxes, each containing 72 cans, are taken from the stock to display on the shelves, how many cans remain in stock?

3. In a school with 743 pupils it is estimated that each pupil uses 15 exercise books in a year. At the beginning of the school year there are 2434 new books in stock, and during the year the school receives two deliveries, each of 5500 new books. How many books remain in stock at the end of the school year?

4. A 1600 metre length of road is to be fenced off on both sides. If a roll of fencing is 33 metres long, how many rolls are required, and how much is left over?

5. A catering pack for a certain jam contains 5000 grams of jam. If 12 grams of jam is used in each jam tart, how many tarts may be made from five catering packs?

6. Thirty-two children in a class collect tokens in order to send for games which are advertised on a cornflakes packet. Each child collects 17 tokens and 50 tokens are required for each game. How many games would they be able to send for?

7. A bookseller purchases 42 packets of a new book, each packet containing 24 books. He stores them in his shop on shelves. How many shelves would be required if each shelf will house 56 books?

8. At a concert 245 people pay £8 each, 413 pay £5 each and 349 pay £3 each. Calculate (a) the total receipts, (b) the profit after expenses of £3785 have been paid.

9. It costs £17 925 for an aeroplane to fly between two cities. If 264 passengers make the flight, travelling either first class or tourist, calculate the profit on the flight given that the 52 first class passengers each pay a fare twice that of the tourist class passenger's fare of £63.

10. A lorry proprietor owns twelve 20 tonne lorries, five 15 tonne lorries and forty-two 10 tonne lorries. How many journeys would each lorry make to remove 30 870 tonnes of materials, assuming that all the lorries make the same number of journeys?

SEQUENCES AND SERIES

Consider the sets of numbers:

(a) 2, 4, 6, 8, ...
(b) 4, 16, 36, 64, ...

In each set the numbers are in a definite order and there is a rule for obtaining any number from the number which comes before it. For example in (a) the even numbers are listed in order, the next two being 10 and 12, whereas in (b) the even numbers have been squared, the next two being 100 and 144. Such a set of numbers is called a *sequence*.

When terms are added together we have a *series*. Thus $2 + 4 + 6 + 8 + 10 + 12$ ... and $4 + 16 + 36 + 64 + ...$ are examples of series. Whether we consider the next term for a sequence or for a series, the rule for finding it is the same.

EXAMPLE 1   Write down the next two terms in the sequence $0, 3, 8, 15, ...$.

The next two terms will be 24 and 35 since the sequence is formed by squaring the natural numbers $1, 2, 3, 4, 5, 6, ...$, and subtracting 1 each time; or $0, {}^{+3}3, {}^{+5}8, {}^{+7}15, {}^{+9}24, {}^{+11}35$.

13

EXAMPLE 2   Write down the next two terms in the sequence 1, 3, 9, 27, ...

This time the rule is to multiply the preceding term by 3. The next two terms are therefore 81 and 243.

EXAMPLE 3   Find the next two terms in the series $1 + 7 + 15 + 25 + \ldots$.

The rth term is $r^2 + 3(r-1)$

i.e. $r = 1$ gives $1^2 + 3(1-1) = 1$
       $r = 2$ gives $2^2 + 3(2-1) = 7$
       $r = 3$ gives $3^2 + 3(3-1) = 15$
       $r = 4$ gives $4^2 + 3(4-1) = 25$
       $r = 5$ gives $5^2 + 3(5-1) = 37$
       $r = 6$ gives $6^2 + 3(6-1) = 51$

$\therefore$ The next two terms are 37 and 51.

EXERCISE 7

Find the next two terms in each of the following sequences:

1. $1, 2, 3, 4, \ldots$
2. $4, 0, -4, -8, \ldots$
3. $4, 6, 8, 10, \ldots$
4. $1, 2, 4, 8, \ldots$
5. $4, 7, 10, 13, 16, \ldots$
6. $24, 12, 6, 3, \ldots$
7. $1, 8, 27, 64, \ldots$
8. $3, -4, -11, \ldots$
9. $1, -8, 27, -64, \ldots$
10. $20, 27, 34, 41, \ldots$
11. $1, -2, -5, -8, \ldots$
12. $8, 4, 1, -1, \ldots$
13. $3, 7, 12, 18, \ldots$
14. $0, 2, 6, 12, \ldots$.

Find the next two terms in each of the following series:

15. $1 + 3 + 5 + 7 + \ldots$
16. $1 + 4 + 9 + 16 + \ldots$
17. $10 + 15 + 20 + 25 + \ldots$
18. $1 - 4 + 9 - 16 + \ldots$
19. $30 + 20 + 10 + \ldots$
20. $10 + 9 + 8 + 7 + \ldots$
21. $12 - 10 + 8 - 6 + \ldots$
22. $50 - 35 + 20 - 5 + \ldots$
23. $100 + 10 + 1 + \ldots$
24. $100 + 20 + 4 + \ldots$
25. $19 + 15 + 11 + 7 \ldots$
26. $3 + 5 + 9 + 17 + \ldots$
27. $19 + 18 + 16 + 13 + \ldots$
28. $72 + 50 + 32 + 18 + \ldots$
29. $-11 + 7 - 3 + \ldots$
30. $0 + 4 + 18 + 48 + \ldots$.

2

FACTORS
AND MULTIPLES

PRIME NUMBERS

Since 12 is exactly divisible by 2 we say that 2 is a *factor* of 12, and 12 is a *multiple* of 2. Similarly, 2, 3, 4 and 6 are factors of 24 and 24 is a multiple of each of the numbers 2, 3, 4 and 6. A number which has no factor apart from itself and 1 is called a *prime number*. Prime numbers in ascending order are 2, 3, 5, 7, 11, 13, 17, 19, 23, 29, 31, ... (Note that 1 is not a prime number.)

It is often convenient to express a number in terms of prime numbers

e.g. $\qquad 12 = 2 \times 2 \times 3$

and $\qquad 378 = 2 \times 3 \times 3 \times 3 \times 7$

In mathematics we are often trying to reduce the amount of writing, and here we can write:

$\qquad 2 \times 2 \qquad$ as $\qquad 2^2$

and $\qquad 3 \times 3 \times 3 \qquad$ as $\qquad 3^3$

We read these as '2 *to the power or index of* 2', or two squared and '3 *to the power or index of* 3' or three cubed.

Similarly $\qquad 5 \times 5 \times 5 \times 5 = 5^4 \qquad$ (5 to the power 4)

and $\qquad 7 \times 7 \times 7 = 7^3 \qquad$ (7 to the power 3)

Extending the idea to the two numbers given above:

$\qquad 12 = 2^2 \times 3 \qquad$ and $\qquad 378 = 2 \times 3^3 \times 7$

15

EXAMPLE 1   Express $2 \times 2 \times 3 \times 3 \times 3 \times 5 \times 3 \times 2$ in index form.

In index form this becomes $2^3 \times 3^4 \times 5$.

EXAMPLE 2   Multiply $2^4 \times 2^3$.

$$2^4 \times 2^3 = (2 \times 2 \times 2 \times 2) \times (2 \times 2 \times 2)$$
$$= 2 \times 2 \times 2 \times 2 \times 2 \times 2 \times 2$$
$$= 2^7$$

(Note that the indices are *added* together i.e. $4 + 3 = 7$.)

Similarly $3^5 \times 3^2 = 3^7$

and $5^8 \times 5^3 = 5^{11}$

EXAMPLE 3   Find the value of $3^3 \times 5^2$.

$$3^3 \times 5^2 = 27 \times 25$$
$$= 675$$

EXAMPLE 4   Express $3^4 \times 3^5 \div 3^7$ in prime factors in index form.

$$\frac{3^4 \times 3^5}{3^7} = \frac{3^9}{3^7} \qquad \textit{(Add the indices when multiplying)}$$

$$= 3^2 \qquad \textit{(Subtract the indices when dividing)}$$

EXAMPLE 5   Express 5096 in prime factors.

$$
\begin{array}{r|r}
2 & 5096 \\
2 & 2548 \\
2 & 1274 \\
7 & 637 \\
7 & 91 \\
13 & 13 \\
\hline
 & 1
\end{array}
$$

$\therefore 5096 = 2^3 \times 7^2 \times 13$

The square root of a number is the number which when multiplied by itself gives the given number. It is denoted by the symbol $\sqrt{\ }$.

e.g. $\sqrt{16} = 4$ since $4 \times 4 = 16$

$\sqrt{144} = 12$ since $12 \times 12 = 144$

EXAMPLE 6   Express 19 600 in prime factors and hence find its square root.

```
2 | 19 600
2 |  9800
2 |  4900
2 |  2450
5 |  1225
5 |   245
7 |    49
7 |     7
  |     1
```

$\therefore$ 19 600 $= 2^4 \times 5^2 \times 7^2$

or 19 600 $= (2^2 \times 5 \times 7) \times (2^2 \times 5 \times 7)$

$= (2^2 \times 5 \times 7)^2$

$\therefore \sqrt{19\,600} = 2^2 \times 5 \times 7 = 140$

i.e. the square root is found by halving each index.

Similarly $\sqrt{54\,756} = \sqrt{2^2 \times 3^4 \times 13^2} = 2 \times 3^2 \times 13 = 234.$

EXERCISE 8

Express the following in prime factors in index form:

1. $3 \times 3 \times 3 \times 5 \times 7 \times 7 \times 5 \times 3$
2. $2 \times 2 \times 11 \times 11 \times 11$
3. $3 \times 2 \times 2 \times 5 \times 2 \times 2 \times 5 \times 2$
4. $3 \times 3 \times 5 \times 7 \times 3 \times 5 \times 5 \times 7$
5. $3^2 \times 3^5$
6. $2^4 \times 2^2 \times 2$
7. $5^8 \div 5^4$
8. $3^4 \times 3^2 \div 3^3$
9. 3×12
10. $4 \times 8 \times 16$
11. $10^2 \times 10^3$
12. $10^3 \times 10^4 \div 100$
13. $2^5 \times 2^2 \div 2^3$
14. $5^5 \div (5^2 \times 5^3)$
15. $12 \times 27.$

Find the values of:

16. $2^2 \times 3^2$
17. $2^2 \times 3^2 \times 5$
18. $2^3 \times 3^2 \times 5^2$
19. $2^4 \times 3^3$
20. $2^2 \times 3^3 \times 5^2.$

Express the following in prime factors:

21. 36
22. 48
23. 108
24. 252
25. 144
26. 675
27. 1715
28. 216
29. 1568
30. 210
31. 864
32. 875
33. 1125
34. 2835
35. 6075
36. 1280
37. 1936
38. 1144
39. 41 503
40. 30 030.

Which of the following numbers are perfect squares?

41. $2^2 \times 3^2 \times 5$ **42.** $2^4 \times 3^2 \times 5^2$

43. $2^4 \times 3^2 \times 11^2$ **44.** $3^3 \times 5^2$

45. $3^2 \times 5^4$ **46.** $2^2 \times 3^3 \times 5^2$

47. $3^4 \times 5^6$ **48.** $2^4 \times 3 \times 7^3$.

Which of the following numbers are perfect cubes?

49. $2^2 \times 3^3$ **50.** $3^3 \times 5^6$ **51.** $2^3 \times 5^2$ **52.** $2^3 \times 5^9$.

What is the least integer (whole number) by which the following numbers must be multiplied to make them perfect squares?

53. $2^3 \times 3^2$ **54.** 2×3^3 **55.** $2^2 \times 3^3 \times 5$

56. $2^4 \times 3^3 \times 7^2$.

What is the least integer by which the following numbers must be multiplied to make them perfect cubes?

57. $2^3 \times 3^2$ **58.** $2^6 \times 3 \times 5^3$ **59.** $2^4 \times 7^3$

60. $3^3 \times 5^6 \times 7^8$.

61. What is the smallest number by which 441 must be multiplied to make it a multiple of 42?

62. What is the smallest number by which 360 must be multiplied to make it a multiple of 35?

63. What is the smallest number by which 1600 must be multiplied to make it a multiple of 84?

Express each of the following numbers in prime factors using index notation and hence find their square roots:

64. 576   **65.** 2025   **66.** 1225   **67.** 2304

68. 2916   **69.** 5184   **70.** 5625   **71.** 193 600.

Express each of the following in prime numbers using index notation and hence find their cube roots:

72. 216   **73.** 729   **74.** 1728   **75.** 3375

76. 5832   **77.** 13 824.

Find the least integers by which the following numbers must be multiplied to make them perfect squares. Find the square roots of the resulting products:

78. 5200   **79.** 1188   **80.** 15 125   **81.** 18 375.

Find the least integers by which the following numbers must be multiplied to make them perfect cubes. Find the cube roots of the resulting products:

82. 72   83. 864   84. 27 783   85. 8575.

HIGHEST COMMON FACTOR (HCF)

A number which is a factor of two or more numbers is a common factor, e.g. 4 is a factor of 12 and 20 and thus it is a common factor of these two numbers. The largest number which is a common factor of two or more numbers is called the *highest common factor* or HCF. In the above example the HCF is 4.

Probably the easiest way of finding the HCF of two or more numbers is to express the numbers in powers of prime factors.

EXAMPLE 7   Find the HCF of 72, 252 and 600.

Expressing each number as powers of prime factors:

$$72 = 2^3 \times 3^2$$
$$252 = 2^2 \times 3^2 \times 7$$
$$600 = 2^3 \times 3 \times 5^2$$

The highest power of 2 which is a factor of each is 2^2, and the highest power of 3 is 3^1, there being no other common factor.

$$\therefore HCF = 2^2 \times 3 = 12$$

It is worth noticing that any common factor of a given set of numbers is also a factor of their difference. This can often be of use in spotting common factors.

LEAST COMMON MULTIPLE (LCM)

The *least common multiple* of two or more numbers is the least number into which each of them will divide without remainder.

EXAMPLE 8   Write down the LCM of 8 and 10.

By inspection the least common multiple of these two numbers is 40.

19

EXAMPLE 9 Write down the LCM of $2^2 \times 3 \times 7$ and 2×3^2 in index form.

$$LCM = 2^2 \times 3^2 \times 7$$

Each of the factors 2, 3 and 7 must be included in the LCM, the power used being the highest occurring.

EXAMPLE 10 Find the LCM of 1176, 630, 300 and 1323.

Expressing each number in prime factors in index form:

$$1176 = 2^3 \times 3 \times 7^2$$
$$630 = 2 \times 3^2 \times 5 \times 7$$
$$300 = 2^2 \times 3 \times 5^2$$
$$1323 = 3^3 \times 7^2$$

The LCM is found by taking every factor which is found in these to the highest power occurring.

Thus $LCM = 2^3 \times 3^3 \times 7^2 \times 5^2$

Since LCMs are often very large numbers they are normally left in factor form.

EXERCISE 9

Write down by inspection the HCF of:

1. 12, 16   2. 20, 30   3. 15, 20, 25   4. 18, 48
5. 12, 18   6. 51, 34   7. 8, 10, 16
8. 30, 45, 60   9. 18, 27   10. 35, 42
11. 12, 18, 42   12. 49, 84   13. 6, 12, 32
14. 9, 24, 39   15. 64, 72   16. 35, 52, 56
17. 18, 54, 72   18. 85, 68   19. 18, 27, 105
20. 42, 70, 84.

Find the HCF of the following sets of numbers, giving your answers as products of prime factors:

21. 45, 60   22. 245, 385   23. 333, 243   24. 175, 448
25. 96, 720   26. 324, 720   27. 120, 408   28. 351, 648
29. 24, 42, 54   30. 432, 768
31. 108, 162, 270   32. 224, 504, 952
33. 96, 192, 216   34. 105, 147, 196

35. $378, 462, 630$ 36. $624, 832, 1072$

37. $275, 100, 225$ 38. $1485, 4725$

39. $168, 392, 448$ 40. $456, 551, 589$

41. $224, 352, 600$ 42. $432, 558, 702$

43. $273, 975, 1638$ 44. $476, 672, 812$

45. $350, 425, 600$ 46. $294, 735, 1323$

47. $882, 1134, 1638$ 48. $792, 1296, 1728$

49. $504, 952, 1176$ 50. $420, 525, 735.$

EXERCISE 10

Write down the LCM of:

1. $5, 10$ 2. $10, 25$ 3. $12, 36$ 4. $3, 4, 5$

5. $9, 18, 36$ 6. $5, 15, 20$ 7. $9, 18, 27$ 8. $21, 28$

9. $15, 30, 60$ 10. $3, 5, 7.$

Write down, in index form, the LCM of:

11. $2 \times 3^2, 2^2 \times 3$ 12. $2^3 \times 5, 2^2 \times 5^2$

13. $2^2 \times 3^4, 2^2 \times 3^2$ 14. $2^2 \times 5, 2 \times 5^3$

15. $2^2 \times 3^2, 2 \times 3^4$ 16. $3^2 \times 5, 3^3 \times 5^2$

17. $3 \times 5^3, 3^3 \times 5$ 18. $2^2 \times 3 \times 5, 3^2 \times 5^3$

19. $2 \times 3^2 \times 5, 2^2 \times 3$ 20. $2^4 \times 3 \times 5^2, 2^2 \times 3^3 \times 5^2.$

Find the LCM of the following, giving your answers in prime factors:

21. $5, 10, 15$ 22. $16, 18, 24$

23. $16, 56, 84$ 24. $63, 81, 147$

25. $100, 125, 150$ 26. $27, 36, 42$

27. $64, 80, 84$ 28. $39, 104, 169$

29. $44, 121, 66$ 30. $36, 48, 108$

31. $18, 24, 36, 42$ 32. $12, 21, 28, 42$

33. $25, 35, 45, 65$ 34. $66, 121, 143, 165$

35. $84, 63, 36, 108.$

3

FRACTIONS

COMMON FRACTIONS

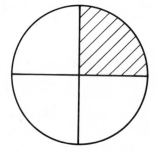

The diagram illustrates an apple tart which is divided into four equal parts (called quarters) for a family with very healthy appetites. The shaded area represents one of these parts and is one-quarter of the whole. This is written $\frac{1}{4}$ and is called a fraction. The lower number (or in this case the number of parts we divide the whole into) is called the *denominator*. The upper number indicates the number of fourth parts taken, and is called the *numerator*. Similarly the unshaded area represents three pieces, each of which is one-quarter of the whole. We write this as $\frac{3}{4}$, the denominator is 4 and the numerator 3.

EXERCISE 11

1. Write the following as fractions: one-half, five-eighths, seven-twentieths, thirteen-sixty-fourths, nine-thirty-seconds.

2. Write the following fractions in words:

   $$\frac{9}{20}, \frac{3}{8}, \frac{21}{29}, \frac{31}{100}, \frac{137}{200}.$$

3. Write down the value of: half of 10 p, three-quarters of £1, seven-eighths of £2, four-twentieths of 1 metre, one-tenth of an hour, two-thirds of a day.

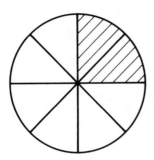

To return to our apple tart, if it had been divided into eight equal parts, each part as a fraction would be written $\frac{1}{8}$. The shaded area is two such parts or $\frac{2}{8}$ and is obviously exactly the same as the shaded area given earlier i.e. $\frac{2}{8} = \frac{1}{4}$.

Similarly we could show that $\frac{5}{20} = \frac{4}{16} = \frac{3}{12} = \frac{2}{8} = \frac{1}{4}$.

All these fractions are equal in value. We thus see that the value of a fraction is unchanged if the numerator and denominator are divided (or multiplied) by the same number.

Thus
$$\frac{12}{18} = \frac{2}{3} = \frac{30}{45}$$

EXAMPLE 1 Reduce $\frac{63}{81}$ to its lowest terms.

Dividing the numerator and denominator by 9 gives:

$$\frac{63}{81} = \frac{7}{9}$$

EXAMPLE 2 Reduce $\frac{1260}{2016}$ to its lowest terms.

$$\frac{1260}{2016} = \frac{315}{504} \qquad \text{(dividing numerator and denominator by 4)}$$

$$= \frac{45}{72} \qquad \text{(dividing numerator and denominator by 7)}$$

$$= \frac{5}{8} \qquad \text{(dividing numerator and denominator by 9)}$$

$$\therefore \quad \frac{1260}{2016} = \frac{5}{8}$$

23

EXAMPLE 3   Express $\dfrac{5}{9}$ with a denominator of 36.

$$\frac{5}{9} = \frac{20}{36} \qquad \text{(multiplying top and bottom by 4)}$$

It is frequently convenient to place fractions in ascending or descending order by expressing all of them with the same denominator.

EXAMPLE 4   Arrange the following in ascending order:

$$\frac{1}{2}, \frac{5}{8}, \frac{9}{12}, \frac{7}{16}.$$

We require the LCM of the denominator, i.e. the lowest number they will all divide into exactly. LCM is 48.

Then $\dfrac{1}{2} = \dfrac{24}{48}, \quad \dfrac{5}{8} = \dfrac{30}{48}, \quad \dfrac{9}{12} = \dfrac{36}{48}, \quad \dfrac{7}{16} = \dfrac{21}{48}$

i.e. the numbers placed in ascending order are $\dfrac{21}{48}, \dfrac{24}{48}, \dfrac{30}{48}, \dfrac{36}{48}$ or $\dfrac{7}{16}, \dfrac{1}{2}, \dfrac{5}{8}, \dfrac{9}{12}.$

EXAMPLE 5   Arrange the following in descending order:

$$\frac{1}{4}, \frac{9}{16}, \frac{3}{5}, \frac{7}{20}.$$

The LCM of the denominator is 80.

Then $\dfrac{1}{4} = \dfrac{20}{80}, \quad \dfrac{9}{16} = \dfrac{45}{80}, \quad \dfrac{3}{5} = \dfrac{48}{80}, \quad \dfrac{11}{20} = \dfrac{44}{80}$

i.e. the numbers placed in descending order are $\dfrac{48}{80}, \dfrac{45}{80}, \dfrac{44}{80}, \dfrac{20}{80}$ or $\dfrac{3}{5}, \dfrac{9}{16}, \dfrac{11}{20}, \dfrac{1}{4}.$

A fraction in which the numerator is less than the denominator is called a *proper fraction* e.g. $\frac{1}{2}, \frac{3}{4}, \frac{4}{5}$, etc., whereas a fraction in which the numerator is greater than the denominator is called an *improper fraction* e.g. $\frac{3}{2}, \frac{4}{3}, \frac{5}{4}$, etc.

Both proper and improper fractions are examples of common or vulgar fractions.

An improper fraction may be expressed as a *mixed number*, consisting of a whole number together with a fraction.

e.g.

$$\frac{5}{4} = \frac{4}{4} + \frac{1}{4}$$

$$= 1 + \frac{1}{4}$$

$$= 1\tfrac{1}{4}$$

and

$$\frac{31}{9} = \frac{27}{9} + \frac{4}{9}$$

$$= 3 + \frac{4}{9}$$

$$= 3\tfrac{4}{9}$$

Do not leave an answer as an improper fraction — change it to a mixed number.

EXERCISE 12

1. Reduce the following fractions to their lowest terms:

   (a) $\dfrac{36}{60}$ (b) $\dfrac{75}{100}$ (c) $\dfrac{144}{324}$ (d) $\dfrac{48}{400}$

   (e) $\dfrac{63}{112}$ (f) $\dfrac{115}{276}$ (g) $\dfrac{362}{676}$ (h) $\dfrac{147}{315}$

   (i) $\dfrac{529}{667}$ (j) $\dfrac{207}{351}$ (k) $\dfrac{252}{684}$ (l) $\dfrac{272}{952}$

   (m) $\dfrac{714}{882}$ (n) $\dfrac{465}{540}$ (o) $\dfrac{1368}{1728}$.

2. Complete:

   (a) $\dfrac{3}{4} = \dfrac{}{16}$ (b) $\dfrac{3}{4} = \dfrac{15}{}$ (c) $\dfrac{2}{5} = \dfrac{}{20}$ (d) $\dfrac{5}{9} = \dfrac{35}{}$

   (e) $\dfrac{8}{7} = \dfrac{}{56}$ (f) $\dfrac{2}{9} = \dfrac{}{63}$ (g) $\dfrac{}{11} = \dfrac{96}{132}$

   (h) $\dfrac{7}{} = \dfrac{56}{64}$ (i) $\dfrac{5}{} = \dfrac{65}{117}$ (j) $\dfrac{7}{12} = \dfrac{252}{}$.

3. Arrange the following fractions in ascending order:

   (a) $\dfrac{1}{4}, \dfrac{1}{3}, \dfrac{3}{8}$ (b) $\dfrac{5}{9}, \dfrac{4}{7}, \dfrac{2}{3}$

   (c) $\dfrac{1}{3}, \dfrac{7}{16}, \dfrac{7}{20}$ (d) $\dfrac{7}{16}, \dfrac{3}{8}, \dfrac{5}{12}, \dfrac{23}{48}$

(e) $\dfrac{41}{45}, \dfrac{31}{36}, \dfrac{15}{16}, \dfrac{77}{81}$

(f) $\dfrac{49}{120}, \dfrac{23}{60}, \dfrac{13}{30}, \dfrac{37}{90}$

(g) $\dfrac{22}{45}, \dfrac{29}{60}, \dfrac{39}{80}, \dfrac{12}{25}$

(h) $\dfrac{7}{30}, \dfrac{13}{60}, \dfrac{2}{9}, \dfrac{4}{15}.$

4. Arrange the following fractions in descending order:

(a) $\dfrac{3}{4}, \dfrac{5}{8}, \dfrac{11}{16}$

(b) $\dfrac{8}{25}, \dfrac{36}{125}, \dfrac{1}{5}$

(c) $\dfrac{5}{7}, \dfrac{11}{14}, \dfrac{13}{20}$

(d) $\dfrac{4}{9}, \dfrac{1}{3}, \dfrac{2}{7}, \dfrac{1}{5}$

(e) $\dfrac{2}{3}, \dfrac{9}{14}, \dfrac{11}{18}, \dfrac{10}{21}$

(f) $\dfrac{2}{9}, \dfrac{5}{21}, \dfrac{2}{7}, \dfrac{5}{28}$

(g) $\dfrac{11}{12}, \dfrac{19}{24}, \dfrac{13}{15}, \dfrac{23}{32}$

(h) $\dfrac{11}{42}, \dfrac{7}{30}, \dfrac{8}{35}, \dfrac{13}{60}.$

5. Express as mixed or whole numbers:

(a) $\dfrac{40}{12}$ (b) $\dfrac{12}{8}$ (c) $\dfrac{44}{3}$ (d) $\dfrac{15}{3}$

(e) $\dfrac{60}{15}$ (f) $\dfrac{70}{13}$ (g) $\dfrac{520}{13}$ (h) $\dfrac{29}{4}$

(i) $\dfrac{37}{8}$ (j) $\dfrac{420}{14}$ (k) $\dfrac{45}{8}$ (l) $\dfrac{94}{13}$

(m) $\dfrac{73}{21}$ (n) $\dfrac{112}{8}$ (o) $\dfrac{51}{13}$ (p) $\dfrac{72}{16}$

(q) $\dfrac{666}{24}$ (r) $\dfrac{241}{19}$ (s) $\dfrac{68}{31}$ (t) $\dfrac{1550}{73}.$

6. Express as improper fractions:

(a) $5\frac{1}{3}$ (b) $4\frac{3}{7}$ (c) $10\frac{1}{9}$ (d) $13\frac{2}{3}$

(e) $14\frac{1}{4}$ (f) $7\frac{3}{4}$ (g) $8\frac{2}{5}$ (h) $9\frac{5}{8}$

(i) $21\frac{1}{6}$ (j) $14\frac{8}{11}$ (k) $16\frac{1}{5}$ (l) $42\frac{4}{9}$

(m) $6\frac{16}{19}$ (n) $4\frac{29}{32}$ (o) $7\frac{11}{31}$ (p) $14\frac{2}{23}$

(q) $72\frac{4}{7}$ (r) $37\frac{5}{8}$ (s) $102\frac{3}{7}$ (t) $240\frac{5}{17}.$

ADDITION

The fractions to be added must be rewritten so that they all have a common denominator.

EXAMPLE 6   Simplify $\dfrac{1}{4} + \dfrac{2}{3}$.

The common denominator of 4 and 3 is 12. We therefore express each fraction in twelfths

i.e. $\dfrac{1}{4} + \dfrac{2}{3} = \dfrac{3}{12} + \dfrac{8}{12}$

$$= \dfrac{11}{12}$$

EXAMPLE 7   Simplify $\dfrac{1}{5} + \dfrac{1}{3} + \dfrac{3}{7}$.

The common denominator is 105.

Then $\dfrac{1}{5} + \dfrac{1}{3} + \dfrac{3}{7} = \dfrac{21}{105} + \dfrac{35}{105} + \dfrac{45}{105}$

$$= \dfrac{101}{105}$$

EXAMPLE 8   Simplify $\dfrac{4}{5} + \dfrac{1}{3} + \dfrac{11}{15}$.

The common denominator is 15.

Then $\dfrac{4}{5} + \dfrac{1}{3} + \dfrac{11}{15} = \dfrac{12}{15} + \dfrac{5}{15} + \dfrac{11}{15}$

$$= \dfrac{28}{15}$$

$$= 1\tfrac{13}{15}$$

When a question involves whole numbers or improper fractions it is usual in addition questions to express any improper fraction as a mixed number and to total the whole numbers before considering the fractions.

EXAMPLE 9   Simplify $5\dfrac{1}{3} + 3\dfrac{3}{4} + 7\dfrac{2}{5}$.

$$5\dfrac{1}{3} + 3\dfrac{3}{4} + 7\dfrac{2}{5} = 5 + 3 + 7 + \dfrac{1}{3} + \dfrac{3}{4} + \dfrac{2}{5}$$

$$= 15 + \frac{20}{60} + \frac{45}{60} + \frac{24}{60}$$

(expressing each fraction in terms of the common denominator)

$$= 15 + \frac{89}{60}$$

$$= 15 + 1 + \frac{29}{60}$$

$$= 16\tfrac{29}{60}$$

When the method is fully understood the solution may be set out as follows:

$$5\frac{1}{3} + 3\frac{3}{4} + 7\frac{2}{5} = 15\frac{20 + 45 + 24}{60}$$

$$= 15\tfrac{89}{60}$$

$$= 16\tfrac{29}{60}$$

EXAMPLE 10 Simplify $4\dfrac{2}{7} + \dfrac{22}{9} + \dfrac{61}{14}$.

$$4\frac{2}{7} + \frac{22}{9} + \frac{61}{14} = 4\frac{2}{7} + 2\frac{4}{9} + 4\frac{5}{14}$$

$$= 10\frac{36 + 56 + 45}{126}$$

$$= 10\tfrac{137}{126}$$

$$= 11\tfrac{11}{126}$$

EXERCISE 13

Simplify:

1. $\dfrac{3}{10} + \dfrac{7}{10}$

2. $\dfrac{3}{15} + \dfrac{7}{15}$

3. $\dfrac{5}{17} + \dfrac{4}{17}$

4. $\dfrac{1}{12} + \dfrac{5}{12}$

5. $\dfrac{9}{20} + \dfrac{3}{20}$

6. $\dfrac{5}{8} + \dfrac{3}{8}$

7. $\dfrac{11}{30} + \dfrac{19}{30}$

8. $\dfrac{1}{4} + \dfrac{3}{8}$

9. $\dfrac{7}{8} + \dfrac{7}{12}$

10. $\dfrac{3}{5} + \dfrac{1}{2}$

11. $\dfrac{4}{5} + \dfrac{5}{8}$

12. $\dfrac{3}{11} + \dfrac{5}{9}$

13. $\dfrac{7}{16} + \dfrac{3}{8}$

14. $\dfrac{1}{4} + \dfrac{11}{16}$

15. $\dfrac{19}{32} + \dfrac{3}{8}$

16. $\dfrac{7}{24} + \dfrac{1}{6}$

17. $\dfrac{1}{2} + \dfrac{1}{3} + \dfrac{1}{4}$

18. $\dfrac{2}{5} + \dfrac{1}{3} + \dfrac{3}{4}$

19. $\dfrac{7}{12} + \dfrac{2}{3} + \dfrac{1}{6}$

20. $\dfrac{5}{6} + \dfrac{1}{2} + \dfrac{7}{12}$

21. $\dfrac{4}{15} + \dfrac{7}{10} + \dfrac{3}{5}$

22. $\dfrac{1}{12} + \dfrac{1}{4} + \dfrac{1}{8}$

23. $\dfrac{11}{36} + \dfrac{7}{12} + \dfrac{5}{6}$

24. $\dfrac{2}{3} + \dfrac{7}{18} + \dfrac{5}{6}$

25. $1\dfrac{1}{2} + \dfrac{3}{4}$

26. $2\dfrac{1}{4} + 1\dfrac{1}{2}$

27. $5\dfrac{1}{3} + 2\dfrac{1}{6}$

28. $4\dfrac{3}{4} + 1\dfrac{7}{8}$

29. $7\dfrac{5}{8} + 2\dfrac{1}{2}$

30. $9\dfrac{1}{3} + 4\dfrac{5}{6}$

31. $12\dfrac{1}{2} + 5\dfrac{3}{7}$

32. $2\dfrac{7}{13} + 1\dfrac{1}{2}$

33. $3\dfrac{11}{12} + 1\dfrac{1}{4}$

34. $2\dfrac{3}{7} + 1\dfrac{1}{4}$

35. $3\dfrac{7}{12} + 3\dfrac{5}{8}$

36. $10\dfrac{3}{8} + 4\dfrac{7}{16}$

37. $1\dfrac{3}{4} + \dfrac{2}{5} + 2\dfrac{1}{10}$

38. $3\dfrac{1}{2} + 2\dfrac{1}{4} + 1\dfrac{1}{8}$

39. $7\dfrac{3}{10} + 2\dfrac{5}{8} + 3\dfrac{1}{2}$

40. $5\dfrac{3}{20} + 8\dfrac{1}{5} + 4\dfrac{1}{4}$

41. $4\dfrac{7}{8} + 5\dfrac{3}{4} + 7\dfrac{1}{2}$

42. $1\dfrac{1}{3} + 3\dfrac{5}{6} + \dfrac{1}{2}$

43. $3\dfrac{1}{7} + 1\dfrac{9}{14} + 2\dfrac{1}{2}$

44. $5\dfrac{1}{5} + 3\dfrac{7}{20} + 5\dfrac{3}{4}$

45. $\dfrac{7}{8} + \dfrac{4}{3} + \dfrac{7}{9}$

46. $\dfrac{15}{8} + \dfrac{9}{4} + \dfrac{7}{2}$

47. $\dfrac{25}{18} + \dfrac{13}{6} + \dfrac{23}{12}$

48. $\dfrac{10}{3} + \dfrac{29}{21} + \dfrac{13}{7}$

49. $4\dfrac{2}{3} + \dfrac{16}{9} + \dfrac{41}{18} + 5\dfrac{7}{12}$

50. $\dfrac{73}{15} + \dfrac{41}{10} + 3\dfrac{1}{5} + \dfrac{7}{30}$.

SUBTRACTION

The following examples illustrate subtraction. Whole numbers are dealt with first.

EXAMPLE 11   Simplify $5\dfrac{3}{5} - 2\dfrac{1}{4}$.

$$5\dfrac{3}{5} - 2\dfrac{1}{4} \;=\; 3 + \dfrac{3}{5} - \dfrac{1}{4}$$

$$= \; 3 + \dfrac{12}{20} - \dfrac{5}{20}$$

$$= \; 3 + \dfrac{7}{20}$$

$$= \; 3\tfrac{7}{20}$$

Or if preferred:

$$5\dfrac{3}{5} - 2\dfrac{1}{4} \;=\; 3\dfrac{12-5}{20}$$

$$= \; 3\tfrac{7}{20}$$

EXAMPLE 12   Simplify $7\dfrac{1}{4} - 3\dfrac{4}{9}$.

$$7\dfrac{1}{4} - 3\dfrac{4}{9} \;=\; 4 + \dfrac{1}{4} - \dfrac{4}{9}$$

$$= \; 4 + \dfrac{9-16}{36}$$

$$= \; 3 + \dfrac{36+9-16}{36}$$

$$= \; 3\tfrac{29}{36}$$

We next consider an example involving addition and subtraction.

EXAMPLE 13   Simplify $5\dfrac{1}{3} - 2\dfrac{2}{5} + 3\dfrac{3}{4} - 1\dfrac{7}{8}$.

$$5\frac{1}{3} - 2\frac{2}{5} + 3\frac{3}{4} - 1\frac{7}{8} = 5\frac{40 - 48 + 90 - 105}{120}$$

$$= 5\frac{130 - 153}{120}$$

(combining the whole numbers and expressing the fractions with a common denominator)

$$= 4\frac{120 + 130 - 153}{120} \quad \left(\text{rewriting 5 as } 4 + \frac{120}{120}\right)$$

$$= 4\frac{97}{120}$$

EXERCISE 14

1. $\dfrac{7}{10} - \dfrac{3}{10}$

2. $\dfrac{7}{15} - \dfrac{3}{15}$

3. $\dfrac{7}{12} - \dfrac{1}{12}$

4. $\dfrac{5}{17} - \dfrac{2}{17}$

5. $\dfrac{9}{24} - \dfrac{1}{12}$

6. $\dfrac{3}{4} - \dfrac{1}{3}$

7. $\dfrac{7}{8} - \dfrac{3}{4}$

8. $\dfrac{17}{18} - \dfrac{5}{6}$

9. $\dfrac{19}{32} - \dfrac{3}{8}$

10. $\dfrac{49}{100} - \dfrac{3}{10}$

11. $\dfrac{9}{14} - \dfrac{2}{21}$

12. $\dfrac{19}{48} - \dfrac{3}{24}$

13. $\dfrac{34}{35} - \dfrac{5}{7}$

14. $\dfrac{4}{5} - \dfrac{5}{7}$

15. $\dfrac{7}{16} - \dfrac{3}{8}$

16. $\dfrac{5}{6} - \dfrac{11}{18}$

17. $\dfrac{2}{3} - \dfrac{1}{4} - \dfrac{1}{6}$

18. $\dfrac{11}{12} - \dfrac{1}{4} - \dfrac{2}{3}$

19. $\dfrac{23}{25} - \dfrac{3}{10} - \dfrac{1}{5}$

20. $\dfrac{17}{30} - \dfrac{2}{5} - \dfrac{1}{16}$

21. $\dfrac{5}{6} - \dfrac{5}{12} + \dfrac{1}{2}$

22. $\dfrac{4}{9} + \dfrac{2}{3} - \dfrac{11}{12}$

23. $\dfrac{4}{7} + \dfrac{10}{21} - \dfrac{3}{14}$

24. $\dfrac{19}{20} - \dfrac{3}{5} + \dfrac{3}{4}$

25. $3\dfrac{2}{3} - 2\dfrac{1}{2}$

26. $5\dfrac{3}{4} - 2\dfrac{3}{8}$

27. $7\dfrac{1}{2} - \dfrac{1}{3}$

28. $9\dfrac{7}{12} - 3\dfrac{1}{3}$

29. $4\dfrac{7}{12} - 2\dfrac{1}{6}$

30. $10\dfrac{3}{4} - 7\dfrac{5}{8}$

31. $2\dfrac{1}{2} - 1\dfrac{3}{4}$

32. $6\dfrac{1}{4} - 1\dfrac{5}{8}$

33. $7\dfrac{3}{8} - 4\dfrac{11}{12}$

34. $3\dfrac{7}{20} - 2\dfrac{11}{15}$

35. $12\dfrac{4}{7} - 5\dfrac{1}{3}$

36. $5\dfrac{3}{5} - 3\dfrac{9}{10}$

37. $5\dfrac{7}{8} - 2\dfrac{1}{2} - 1\dfrac{1}{4}$

38. $10 - 2\dfrac{1}{12} - 3\dfrac{5}{6}$

39. $8 - 4\dfrac{4}{7} - 2\dfrac{2}{5}$

40. $6\dfrac{3}{4} - \dfrac{7}{12} - 3\dfrac{9}{16}$

41. $7\dfrac{3}{7} - 2\dfrac{3}{14} - 3\dfrac{1}{2}$

42. $3\dfrac{1}{4} + 4\dfrac{1}{3} - 5\dfrac{1}{6}$

43. $4\dfrac{7}{12} - 3\dfrac{5}{8} + 1\dfrac{2}{3}$

44. $12\dfrac{1}{4} - 7\dfrac{5}{6} + 4\dfrac{11}{12}$

45. $\dfrac{11}{6} - \dfrac{4}{3} - \dfrac{4}{9}$

46. $\dfrac{21}{4} - \dfrac{5}{3} - \dfrac{7}{2}$

47. $\dfrac{52}{25} + \dfrac{12}{5} - \dfrac{23}{20}$

48. $\dfrac{49}{36} + \dfrac{17}{12} - \dfrac{9}{8}$

49. $5\dfrac{1}{3} - \dfrac{19}{4} + \dfrac{31}{6} - 2\dfrac{1}{2}$

50. $\dfrac{17}{5} + 5\dfrac{1}{4} - \dfrac{33}{8} - \dfrac{11}{10}$

MULTIPLICATION

If 4 boys each have £$\frac{1}{5}$, then the total amount of money they have between them is:

$$£\left(\frac{1}{5} + \frac{1}{5} + \frac{1}{5} + \frac{1}{5}\right) = £\frac{4}{5}$$

or

$$4 \times £\frac{1}{5} = £\frac{4}{5}$$

i.e. to multiply a fraction by an integer we multiply the numerator by that integer, leaving the denominator unchanged.

e.g.

$$3 \times \frac{1}{7} = \frac{3}{7}, \qquad 5 \times \frac{2}{13} = \frac{10}{13},$$

$$7 \times \frac{3}{14} = \frac{21}{14} = \frac{3}{2} = 1\frac{1}{2}$$

A simple solution for $7 \times \dfrac{3}{14}$ would be to write $7 \times \dfrac{3}{14} = \dfrac{3}{2}$ (dividing numerator and denominator by 7).

To multiply proper fractions together, multiply their numerators to give the numerator of the answer, and their denominators to give the denominator of the answer.

e.g. $$\frac{5}{7} \times \frac{3}{4} = \frac{15}{28} \quad \text{and} \quad \frac{7}{12} \times \frac{13}{23} = \frac{91}{276}$$

If a mixed number is involved it must first be expressed as an improper fraction

thus $$1\frac{1}{2} \times \frac{7}{8} = \frac{3}{2} \times \frac{7}{8} = \frac{21}{16} = 1\frac{5}{16}$$

and $$4\frac{1}{4} \times 2\frac{1}{2} = \frac{17}{4} \times \frac{5}{2} = \frac{85}{8} = 10\frac{5}{8}$$

Frequently a number will divide into the numerator of one of the fractions being multiplied and the denominator of another thus simplifying the calculations.

e.g. $$7\frac{1}{2} \times 2\frac{4}{5} = \frac{\overset{3}{\cancel{15}}}{\cancel{2}_{1}} \times \frac{\overset{7}{\cancel{14}}}{\cancel{5}_{1}} = 21$$

and $$3\frac{3}{7} \times 1\frac{5}{12} \times 4\frac{2}{3} = \frac{\overset{2}{\cancel{24}}}{\cancel{7}_{1}} \times \frac{17}{\cancel{12}_{1}} \times \frac{\overset{2}{\cancel{14}}}{3} = \frac{68}{3} = 22\frac{2}{3}$$

(Reducing can only be carried out when the fractions are multiplied. It cannot be done with $\frac{24}{7} + \frac{17}{12}$ or $\frac{24}{7} - \frac{17}{12}$ or $\frac{24}{7} \div \frac{17}{12}$.)

When 'of' occurs between two fractions it may always be replaced by multiplication.

e.g. $$\frac{2}{5} \text{ of } 2\frac{1}{3} \text{ means } \frac{2}{5} \times 2\frac{1}{3} = \frac{2}{5} \times \frac{7}{3} = \frac{14}{15}$$

and $$\frac{8}{9} \text{ of } 5\frac{2}{5} = \frac{8}{9} \times \frac{27}{5} = \frac{24}{5} = 4\frac{4}{5}$$

EXERCISE 15

Find the value of:

1. $\dfrac{7}{8} \text{cm} \times 4$ 2. $\dfrac{3}{4}\text{m} \times 3$ 3. $£\dfrac{7}{12} \times 8$ 4. $\dfrac{5}{13} \times 5$

5. $\dfrac{4}{5}\,\text{p} \times 12$

6. $3 \times \dfrac{7}{2}\,\text{litres}$

7. $5 \times \dfrac{2}{3}\,\text{pints}$

8. $4 \times \dfrac{3}{4}\,\text{gallons}$

9. $12 \times \dfrac{3}{5}\,\text{grams}$

10. $6 \times \dfrac{4}{9}\,\text{seconds}$

11. $8 \times \dfrac{3}{4}\,\text{p}$

12. $9 \times \dfrac{5}{12}\,\text{kg}$

13. $\dfrac{4}{5} \times 12$

14. $\dfrac{3}{25} \times 10$

15. $\dfrac{4}{13} \times 6$

16. $\dfrac{5}{9} \times 24$

17. $10 \times \dfrac{3}{5}$

18. $20 \times \dfrac{7}{4}$

19. $36 \times \dfrac{4}{9}$

20. $27 \times \dfrac{4}{3}$

21. $2\dfrac{1}{4} \times 8$

22. $3\dfrac{2}{3} \times 12$

23. $5\dfrac{1}{7} \times 14$

24. $4\dfrac{7}{8} \times 6$

25. $7 \times 3\dfrac{1}{2}$

26. $13 \times 1\dfrac{1}{4}$

27. $18 \times \dfrac{7}{9}$

28. $15 \times \dfrac{7}{24}$

29. $\dfrac{2}{3} \times \dfrac{5}{9}$

30. $\dfrac{7}{12} \times \dfrac{3}{5}$

31. $\dfrac{8}{13} \times \dfrac{5}{12}$

32. $\dfrac{20}{21} \times \dfrac{7}{4}$

33. $\dfrac{3}{14} \times \dfrac{21}{49}$

34. $\dfrac{7}{64} \times \dfrac{16}{21}$

35. $\dfrac{5}{8}\,\text{of}\,4$

36. $\dfrac{3}{7}\,\text{of}\,\dfrac{14}{19}$

37. $4\dfrac{1}{2} \times \dfrac{4}{9}$

38. $4\dfrac{1}{4} \times \dfrac{13}{34}$

39. $7\dfrac{3}{5} \times \dfrac{5}{19}$

40. $5\dfrac{2}{5} \times \dfrac{7}{8}$

41. $\dfrac{11}{15}\,\text{of}\,2\dfrac{3}{22}$

42. $\dfrac{4}{7}\,\text{of}\,4\dfrac{3}{8}$

43. $2\dfrac{5}{8} \times \dfrac{3}{7} \times 2\dfrac{2}{5}$

44. $\dfrac{2}{17} \times 3\dfrac{1}{8} \times 1\dfrac{7}{10}$

45. $3\dfrac{1}{6} \times 1\dfrac{5}{7} \times 5\dfrac{1}{4}$

46. $3\dfrac{3}{7} \times 1\dfrac{5}{9} \times 2\dfrac{1}{8}$

47. $4\dfrac{1}{2} \times 3\dfrac{2}{3} \times 1\dfrac{1}{11}$

48. $1\dfrac{2}{5} \times 2\dfrac{1}{4} \times 4\dfrac{1}{3}$

49. $\dfrac{2}{3}\,\text{of}\,\left(2\dfrac{1}{2} \times 1\dfrac{4}{5}\right)^{2}$

50. $\left(1\dfrac{5}{7} \times 2\dfrac{1}{3}\right)^{2} \times \dfrac{3}{16}.$

DIVISION

If you divide £1 or 100 p into 4 equal parts you divide it into quarters, e.g. one-quarter of 100 p is 25 p.

$$\text{We write this} \quad \tfrac{1}{4} \times 100p = 25p$$

Thus to divide a number by 4 we multiply it by $\tfrac{1}{4}$

e.g.
$$7 \div 4 = 7 \times \frac{1}{4} = \frac{7}{4} = 1\frac{3}{4}$$

$$\frac{3}{4} \div 4 = \frac{3}{4} \times \frac{1}{4} = \frac{3}{16}$$

Similarly $\dfrac{3}{4}$ divided by $\dfrac{2}{3}$ is written:

$$\frac{3}{4} \div \frac{2}{3} = \frac{3}{4} \times \frac{3}{2} = \frac{9}{8} = 1\frac{1}{8}$$

and
$$\frac{5}{7} \div \frac{3}{4} = \frac{5}{7} \times \frac{4}{3} = \frac{20}{21}$$

To divide a number by a fraction, multiply by the fraction turned upside down. The word we use for this in mathematics is *reciprocal* or *inverse*.

$$\text{The reciprocal of 7 is} \quad \frac{1}{7}$$

$$\text{The reciprocal of} \quad \frac{2}{3} \quad \text{is} \quad \frac{3}{2}$$

$$\text{The reciprocal of} \quad \frac{5}{9} \quad \text{is} \quad \frac{9}{5}$$

$$\text{The reciprocal of} \quad \frac{1}{13} \quad \text{is 13}$$

NOTE: Any number multiplied by its reciprocal gives an answer of 1.

EXAMPLE 14
$$3\frac{1}{5} \div \frac{4}{7} = \frac{16}{5} \div \frac{4}{7}$$

$$= \frac{16}{5} \times \frac{7}{4}$$

$$= \frac{28}{5}$$

$$= 5\frac{3}{5}$$

EXAMPLE 15

$$8\frac{2}{7} \div 5\frac{4}{5} = \frac{58}{7} \div \frac{29}{5}$$

$$= \frac{58}{7} \times \frac{5}{29}$$

$$= \frac{10}{7}$$

$$= 1\frac{3}{7}$$

EXERCISE 16

Find the value of:

1. $\frac{1}{2}$ divided by 4

2. $\frac{1}{3}$ divided by 3

3. $\frac{1}{4}$ divided by 2

4. $\frac{2}{3}$ divided by 7

5. $\frac{5}{13}$ divided by 10

6. $\frac{4}{7}$ divided by 2

7. $2\frac{1}{2}$ divided by 5

8. $7\frac{1}{3}$ divided by 11

9. $4 \div \frac{1}{2}$ 10. $6 \div \frac{1}{3}$ 11. $5 \div \frac{1}{2}$ 12. $12 \div \frac{1}{8}$

13. $\frac{1}{4} \div \frac{1}{2}$ 14. $\frac{1}{2} \div \frac{1}{3}$ 15. $\frac{1}{20} \div \frac{1}{5}$ 16. $\frac{1}{4} \div \frac{1}{20}$

17. $\frac{3}{8} \div \frac{2}{3}$ 18. $\frac{7}{12} \div \frac{2}{5}$ 19. $\frac{8}{9} \div \frac{2}{7}$ 20. $\frac{9}{16} \div \frac{3}{4}$

21. $1 \div \frac{1}{3}$ 22. $1 \div \frac{4}{3}$ 23. $1 \div \frac{9}{10}$ 24. $1 \div \frac{20}{21}$

25. $\frac{15}{4} \div \frac{5}{2}$ 26. $\frac{12}{7} \div \frac{3}{14}$ 27. $\frac{18}{11} \div \frac{27}{22}$ 28. $\frac{5}{13} \div \frac{10}{19}$

29. $1\frac{1}{2} \div \frac{2}{3}$ 30. $2\frac{1}{3} \div 1\frac{5}{9}$ 31. $4\frac{1}{7} \div 2\frac{5}{12}$ 32. $3\frac{3}{5} \div 2\frac{7}{10}$

33. $\dfrac{\frac{1}{3}}{5}$ 34. $\dfrac{\frac{1}{1}}{2\frac{1}{4}}$ 35. $\dfrac{\frac{1}{7}}{3}$ 36. $\dfrac{\frac{1}{4}}{4\frac{4}{7}}$

37. $1\frac{1}{2} \div 1\frac{1}{5}$

38. $5\frac{1}{3} \div 1\frac{1}{7}$

39. $4\frac{2}{5} \div 5\frac{1}{2}$

40. $4\frac{1}{3} \div 9\frac{3}{4}$

41. $8\frac{4}{13} \div 5\frac{2}{5}$

42. $6\frac{2}{5} \div 9\frac{3}{5}$

43. $6\frac{1}{2} \div 2\frac{3}{5}$

44. $9\frac{2}{3} \div 8\frac{2}{7}$

45. $2\frac{5}{8} \div 12\frac{1}{4}$

46. $17\frac{3}{5} \div 3\frac{3}{10}$

47. $6\frac{3}{8} \div 21\frac{1}{4}$

48. $8\frac{1}{8} \div 7\frac{3}{7}$

49. $31\frac{2}{7} \div 4\frac{13}{15}$

50. $5\frac{5}{14} \div 19\frac{4}{9}$.

EXERCISE 17 MISCELLANEOUS EXAMPLES

1. A box contains 120 oranges but $\frac{3}{8}$ of them are found to be bad. How many are satisfactory?

2. My electricity bill for heating and lighting was £324. If $\frac{7}{9}$ of the cost was for heating, how much did I pay for lighting?

3. In a secondary school $\frac{7}{12}$ of the third-year pupils are girls and 105 are boys. How many girls are there?

4. In a mathematics textbook $\frac{2}{5}$ deals with arithmetic, $\frac{3}{7}$ algebra and the remainder geometry. If the book has 210 pages, how many pages of geometry are there?

5. During a 6 hour coach journey the rest periods amount to $\frac{1}{5}$ of the time. If the average speed of the coach when it is moving is 50 mph, how long is the journey?

6. A petrol storage tank is three-quarters full. After 75 gallons have been drawn off it is three-fifths full. What is the capacity of the tank?

7. The local council agrees to pay $\frac{3}{7}$ of the cost of running a leisure centre, with the county council paying the remainder. If the county council pays £490 000, find the total running cost.

8. After spending $\frac{5}{6}$ of my pocket money I have 80 p remaining. How much pocket money do I receive?

9. A man poured $\frac{5}{8}$ of a can of oil into his car engine and had 3 litres left over. How much did he use?

10. A retailer bought a quantity of eggs. 46 were broken, the remainder being $\frac{8}{9}$ of the original. How many eggs did he buy?

11. John and Fred go into business together, John putting up $\frac{7}{12}$ of the capital and Fred the remainder of £10 400. How much did John contribute?

12. Anne, Betty and Cheryl decide to open a hairdressing salon. To do this they require £2680. Anne contributes $\frac{7}{20}$ of it, Betty $\frac{3}{10}$ and Cheryl the remainder. How much does each contribute?

13. In a book containing four short stories, the first is $\frac{1}{6}$ of the whole, the second $\frac{1}{8}$, the third 126 pages and the fourth $\frac{1}{3}$. How many pages are in the book?

14. The product of two numbers is 8. If one of the numbers is $3\frac{1}{3}$, find the other.

15. The product of two numbers is 21. If one of the numbers is $2\frac{4}{7}$, find the other.

16. How many jars, each of which holds $\frac{3}{8}$ kg, may be filled from a tin containing 21 kg?

17. The area of a blackboard is $8\frac{3}{4}$ square metres. If the board is $1\frac{2}{3}$ m wide, how long is it?

18. If it takes $3\frac{1}{3}$ minutes to fill $\frac{3}{8}$ of a water storage tank, how long will it take to fill it completely?

19. When the larger of two fractions is divided by the smaller, the result is $1\frac{7}{18}$. If the smaller fraction is $2\frac{2}{5}$, find the larger.

20. When the smaller of two fractions is divided by the larger, the result is $\frac{7}{9}$. If the smaller fraction is $2\frac{2}{3}$, find the larger.

DECIMALS

DECIMALS AND COMMON FRACTIONS

Consider the number 5555:

$$5555 = 5\,\text{thousands} + 5\,\text{hundreds} + 5\,\text{tens} + 5\,\text{units}$$

Each figure in the number 5555 has a value which is 10 times the value of the number immediately following it. It would seem quite reasonable to extend this system to fractional quantities or quantities which are less than unity. If we place a dot or decimal point at the change-over position from whole numbers to fractional or decimal parts, then

$$5555.555 = 5\,\text{thousands} + 5\,\text{hundreds} + 5\,\text{tens}$$
$$+ 5\,\text{units} + 5\,\text{tenths} + 5\,\text{hundredths}$$
$$+ 5\,\text{thousandths}$$

The decimal point is necessary to determine where the change-over occurs.

Hence
$$.555 = 5\,\text{tenths} + 5\,\text{hundredths} + 5\,\text{thousandths}$$

$$= \frac{5}{10} + \frac{5}{100} + \frac{5}{1000}$$

$$= \frac{555}{1000}$$

A decimal is therefore a fraction whose denominator is a power of 10. As in 505 where the zero tells us that there are no tens, so in .505 there are five tenths, no hundredths and five thousandths. The zero holds the position if all non-zero digits are absent. It is common practice if there is no whole number before the decimal point to write a zero in front of it, e.g. instead of .505 we write 0.505.

Any decimal fraction may be written as a common fraction quite easily, but frequently this fraction is not in its lowest terms.

e.g.
$$0.5 = \frac{5}{10} = \frac{1}{2}$$

and
$$0.555 = \frac{555}{1000} = \frac{111}{200}$$

EXAMPLE 1

Write (a) $\dfrac{7}{10}$, (b) $\dfrac{4}{10} + \dfrac{5}{100} + \dfrac{7}{1000}$ as decimals.

(a) $\dfrac{7}{10} = 0.7$

(b) $\dfrac{4}{10} + \dfrac{5}{100} + \dfrac{7}{1000} = 0.457$

EXAMPLE 2

Express (a) 0.8, (b) 0.359 as the sums of vulgar fractions whose denominators are 10, 100, 1000.

(a) $0.8 = \dfrac{8}{10}$

(b) $0.359 = \dfrac{3}{10} + \dfrac{5}{100} + \dfrac{9}{1000}$

EXAMPLE 3

Express (a) 0.535, (b) 0.074 as single vulgar fractions with a power of 10 as the denominator.

(a) $0.535 = \dfrac{535}{1000}$

(b) $0.074 = \dfrac{74}{1000}$

EXAMPLE 4

Express (a) 0.65, (b) 0.624 as vulgar fractions in their lowest terms.

(a) $0.65 = \dfrac{65}{100} = \dfrac{13}{20}$

(b) $0.624 = \dfrac{624}{1000} = \dfrac{78}{125}$

EXERCISE 18

Rewrite each of the following in decimal form:

	THOUSANDS	HUNDREDS	TENS	UNITS	TENTHS	HUNDREDTHS	THOUSANDTHS
1.			1	2	3		
2.				4	5	6	
3.			8	3	7	3	
4.				7	3	4	6
5.			2	4		5	
6.		1		5	6		4
7.		7	2	6		8	
8.			1		5	3	6
9.		4			2	3	
10.	6	1		4	5		8

Express each of the following in table form as shown above:

11. 8.6 12. 4.27 13. 26.83 14. 4.926

15. 27.942 16. 636.421 17. 16.04 18. 33.005

19. 30.92 20. 406.507 21. 126.543 22. 500.063

23. 735.707 24. 3007.607 25. 7305.042 26. 0.64

27. 0.247 28. 0.093 29. 0.114 30. 0.008.

Write the following as decimals:

31. $\dfrac{3}{10}$ 32. $\dfrac{7}{10}$ 33. $\dfrac{3}{10} + \dfrac{7}{100}$ 34. $\dfrac{5}{10} + \dfrac{4}{100}$

35. $\dfrac{3}{10} + \dfrac{5}{100} + \dfrac{7}{1000}$ 36. $\dfrac{1}{10} + \dfrac{7}{100} + \dfrac{4}{1000}$

37. $\dfrac{35}{100} + \dfrac{2}{1000}$ 38. $\dfrac{49}{100} + \dfrac{7}{1000}$

39. $\dfrac{9}{10} + \dfrac{13}{1000}$ 40. $\dfrac{7}{10} + \dfrac{5}{1000}$

41. $\dfrac{37}{1000}$ 42. $\dfrac{52}{1000}$ 43. $\dfrac{234}{1000}$ 44. $\dfrac{53}{10}$

45. $\dfrac{472}{100}$ 46. $\dfrac{12}{10} + \dfrac{3}{100}$.

Express each of the following as the sum of common fractions whose denominators are 10, 100, 1000, etc.:

47. 0.4   48. 0.27   49. 0.83   50. 0.246

51. 0.737   52. 0.829   53. 0.062   54. 0.0359

55. 5.37   56. 4.29   57. 10.07   58. 35.903.

Express each of the following as a single common fraction with a power of 10 as the denominator:

59. 0.3   60. 0.38   61. 0.94   62. 0.357

63. 0.848   64. 0.718   65. 0.051   66. 0.0248

67. 4.73   68. 82.4   69. 6.945   70. 23.052.

Express each of the following as a common fraction in its lowest terms:

71. 0.8   72. 0.75   73. 0.45   74. 0.65

75. 0.375   76. 0.625   77. 0.64   78. 0.28

79. 0.36   80. 0.628   81. 0.444   82. 0.875

83. 0.55   84. 0.78   85. 0.125.

MULTIPLICATION AND DIVISION BY 10 OR A POWER OF 10

Since $25 \times 10 = 250$, the 5 units when multiplied by 10 become 5 tens and the 2 tens become 2 hundreds i.e. each figure in the original number is moved one place to the left in relation to the decimal point. Put another way, the decimal point is moved one place to the right. In the same way:

$$42.64 \times 10 = 426.4$$

and

$$7.26 \times 100 = 7.26 \times 10 \times 10 = 72.6 \times 10$$
$$= 726$$

i.e. if we multiply by 100 the decimal point is moved two places to the right.

Similarly $\times 1000$ moves the decimal point 3 places to the right,
$\times 10\,000$ moves the decimal point 4 places to the right,

and so on.

Division by 10 makes tens become units, hundreds become tens, and so on.

e.g. $64.2 \div 10 = 6.42$

To divide by 10 we move the decimal point 1 place to the left. Similarly, to divide by 100 we move the decimal point 2 places to the left, to divide by 1000 we move the decimal point 3 places to the left, and so on.

EXAMPLE 5   (a) $927.4 \times 100 = 92\,740$
(b) $50.38 \times 10 = 503.8$
(c) $0.0349 \times 1000 = 34.9$

EXAMPLE 6   (a) $67.4 \div 100 = 0.674$
(b) $423.8 \div 10\,000 = 0.042\,38$
(c) $0.72 \div 1000 = 0.000\,72$

EXERCISE 19

Simplify:

1. 6.73×10
2. 14.21×10
3. 0.892×10
4. 36.14×100
5. 0.0429×100
6. 1.642×100
7. 4.96×1000
8. 0.235×1000
9. 0.0964×1000
10. $0.428 \times 10\,000$
11. 3.943×10
12. 16.92×100
13. 239.2×10
14. 43.68×100
15. 0.912×1000
16. 0.007×1000
17. 1.229×100
18. $0.0264 \times 10\,000$
19. $0.734 \times 10\,000$
20. $0.82 \times 100\,000$
21. $70.2 \div 10$
22. $8.42 \div 10$
23. $246.4 \div 10$
24. $0.526 \div 10$
25. $431.5 \div 100$
26. $62.3 \div 100$
27. $5.176 \div 100$
28. $0.916 \div 100$
29. $734 \div 1000$
30. $1920 \div 1000$

31. $8.264 \div 100$ 32. $43.4 \div 10$

33. $0.9 \div 1000$ 34. $90 \div 100$

35. $742 \div 1000$ 36. $60.6 \div 10$

37. $0.634 \div 100$ 38. $0.074 \div 100$

39. $436 \div 10\,000$ 40. $909.6 \div 1000$.

ADDITION AND SUBTRACTION

Addition and subtraction of decimals are carried out in the same way as with whole numbers. The most important thing to remember is that the decimal points must be placed underneath one another. This ensures that all digits with the same place value are written in the same column.

EXAMPLE 7   Add 5.16, 37.4, 0.361 and 162.04.

$$
\begin{array}{r}
5.16 \\
37.4 \\
0.361 \\
162.04 \\
\hline
204.961 \\
\hline
\end{array}
$$

EXAMPLE 8   Subtract 73.649 from 243.94.

$$
\begin{array}{r}
243.94 \\
73.649 \\
\hline
170.291 \\
\hline
\end{array}
$$

EXERCISE 20

Addition

1. 4.3
   2.5
   ___

2. 7.5
   2.3
   ___

3. 6.1
   1.8
   ___

4. 3.6
   5.2
   ___

5. 3.8
   6.1
   ___

6. 7.3
   1.9
   ___

7. 6.8
   2.7
   ___

8. 4.4
   3.8
   ___

9. 5.9
   7.4
   ___

10. 6.7
    5.8
    ___

11. 7.61
    1.25
    ___

12. 2.33
    5.41
    ___

13. 4.55
    3.43
    ‾‾‾‾

14. 6.45
    7.95
    ‾‾‾‾

15. 8.73
    4.28
    ‾‾‾‾

16. 40.15
    16.23
    ‾‾‾‾

17. 71.04
    13.82
    ‾‾‾‾

18. 32.41
    11.83
    ‾‾‾‾

19. 45.71
    59.09
    ‾‾‾‾

20. 18.72
    52.53
    ‾‾‾‾

21. 17.31
    124.97
    ‾‾‾‾

22. 82.58
    243.04
    ‾‾‾‾

23. 173.4
    59.73
    ‾‾‾‾

24. 521.4
    58.97
    ‾‾‾‾

25. 373.9
    48.62
    ‾‾‾‾

26. 9.372
    14.142
    ‾‾‾‾

27. 15.043
    7.994
    ‾‾‾‾

28. 62.3
    15.895
    ‾‾‾‾

29. 4.437
    0.975
    ‾‾‾‾

30. 37.914
    3.009
    ‾‾‾‾

31. 7.334
    18.21
    54.095
    ‾‾‾‾

32. 16.04
    93.87
    5.927
    ‾‾‾‾

33. 34.92
    27.36
    50.25
    ‾‾‾‾

34. 127.9
    38.72
    5.947
    ‾‾‾‾

35. 4.926
    27.35
    337.9
    ‾‾‾‾

36. 0.536
    1.904
    25.88
    ‾‾‾‾

37. 64.9
    8.345
    136.48
    ‾‾‾‾

38. 31.92
    8.437
    463.8
    ‾‾‾‾

39. 42.76
    90.04
    37.095
    ‾‾‾‾

40. 731.4
    9.537
    38.92
    ‾‾‾‾

41. 50.21
    134.92
    16.73
    58.56
    ‾‾‾‾

42. 4.926
    73.35
    4.728
    516.045
    ‾‾‾‾

43. 6.92
    27.668
    5.931
    48.043
    ‾‾‾‾

44. 76.009
    0.926
    3.741
    54.8
    ‾‾‾‾

45. 344.59
    84.47
    0.927
    36.5
    ‾‾‾‾

46. 540.73
    349.2
    16.34
    9.454
    62.09
    ‾‾‾‾

47. 13.43
    8.2
    9.67
    34.53
    5.98
    ‾‾‾‾

48. 44.91
    33.675
    18.9
    66.35
    0.925
    ‾‾‾‾

49. 842.1
    36.93
    8.445
    0.737
    ‾‾‾‾

50. 2.142
    36.085
    50.92
    845.2
    ‾‾‾‾

Add :

51. $9.4 + 3.7 + 16.2$ **52.** $51.2 + 19.4 + 37.26$

53. $18.09 + 62.14 + 7.9$ **54.** $83.74 + 7.447 + 3.92$

55. $56.92 + 247.1 + 8.993$ **56.** $37.85 + 334.8 + 9.75$

57. $4 + 0.25 + 0.873$ **58.** $15.2 + 3.004 + 1.732$

59. $73.91 + 253.34 + 47.936$ **60.** $22.04 + 85.904 + 17.88.$

Subtraction

61.	8.5 6.3	**62.**	4.9 1.7	**63.**	12.8 1.5	**64.**	36.4 25.2
65.	59.7 35.4	**66.**	5.97 3.45	**67.**	16.82 3.71	**68.**	42.76 31.34
69.	9.453 1.232	**70.**	64.95 53.71	**71.**	32.4 19.3	**72.**	6.74 3.78
73.	72.64 18.25	**74.**	40.92 36.37	**75.**	5.84 1.87	**76.**	40.982 16.389
77.	51.253 34.937	**78.**	341.43 27.94	**79.**	621.42 344.93	**80.**	54.217 3.778
81.	200.43 167.97	**82.**	516.9 47.36	**83.**	16.493 8.56	**84.**	84.17 9.385
85.	4.835 0.996	**86.**	5.6 1.447	**87.**	18.4 7.346	**88.**	50.2 8.345
89.	30.2 19.731	**90.**	84.000 58.886				

91. Subtract 6.49 from 12.97.

92. Subtract 15.23 from 38.09.

93. Subtract 0.935 from 2.

94. Subtract 7.543 from 10.

95. Subtract 249.66 from 500.

96. From 27.2 subtract 7.39.

97. From 84.92 subtract 57.37.

98. From 100 subtract 49.35.

99. From 300 subtract 247.924.

100. From 80 subtract 0.737.

MULTIPLICATION

EXAMPLE 9   Multiply 5.3 by 4.71.

(Rough answer $5 \times 5 = 25$.)

Since $5.3 = \dfrac{53}{10}$ and $4.71 = \dfrac{471}{100}$

$$5.3 \times 4.71 = \frac{53}{10} \times \frac{471}{100} = \frac{24\,963}{1000} = 24.963$$

We may therefore multiply the two numbers together using long multiplication, then count the total number of decimal places *after* the decimal point in the two numbers (1 from 5.3 and 2 from 4.71), and place the decimal point in the answer so that this number of places (i.e. 3) comes *after* the decimal point.

EXAMPLE 10   Find 5.64×3.45.

(Rough answer $6 \times 3 = 18$.)

5.64	2 places after the point
3.45	2 places after the point
2820	
22 560	
169 200	
19.4580	$\therefore$ 4 places after the point in the answer

$\therefore$ $5.64 \times 3.45 = 19.4580$

EXAMPLE 11   Find 70.16×0.293.

(Rough answer $70 \times 0.3 = 21$.)

70.16	2 places after the point
0.293	3 places after the point
21 048	
631 440	
1 403 200	
20.556 88	$\therefore$ 5 places after the point in the answer

$\therefore$ $70.16 \times 0.293 = 20.556\,88$

EXERCISE 21

Find:

1. 0.2×5	2. 0.3×4	3. 0.7×8
4. 0.4×6	5. 0.03×7	6. 0.08×5
7. 0.06×8	8. 0.02×9	9. 0.12×4
10. 0.35×6	11. 0.26×7	12. 0.78×3
13. 1.73×5	14. 2.84×4	15. 5.93×8
16. 7.24×6	17. 6.37×3	18. 8.78×7
19. 7.82×2	20. 9.35×5	21. 0.52×20
22. 0.71×50	23. 0.36×80	24. 0.73×30
25. 0.042×30	26. 0.07×500	27. 0.033×60
28. 4.35×40	29. 8.92×90	30. 36.5×70
31. 7.34×50	32. 4.2×1.3	33. 9.7×2.5
34. 6.9×8.4	35. 3.4×6.3	36. 0.6×0.3
37. 0.7×0.5	38. 0.9×0.8	39. 0.2×0.4
40. 0.54×0.27	41. 0.018×4000	42. 0.34×0.72
43. 0.88×0.51	44. 0.67×0.24	45. 2.42×0.81
46. 0.93×0.24	47. 4.37×0.82	48. 9.16×0.38
49. 36.2×1.4	50. 91.7×2.7	51. 43.6×5.3
52. 70.9×8.6	53. 16.4×7.04	54. 51.6×8.09
55. 36.21×18.2	56. 61.3×37.5	57. 52.41×0.423
58. 4.59×1.237	59. 78.91×4.64	60. 60.24×0.4153

61. $(1.732)^2$	62. $(1.414)^2$
63. $(2.236)^2$	64. $(3.142)^2$
65. 731.4×0.0043	66. $450 \times 0.009\,31$
67. 672×0.0531	68. 89.4×0.0229
69. $0.2 \times 0.3 \times 0.4$	70. $1.2 \times 0.5 \times 0.4$
71. $5.1 \times 0.8 \times 0.4$	72. $2.4 \times 0.5 \times 0.7$
73. $0.3 \times 5.2 \times 0.7$	74. $0.8 \times 3.1 \times 0.5$
75. $0.9 \times 8.2 \times 0.4$	76. $0.6 \times 7.3 \times 0.7$
77. $3.14 \times 0.5 \times 0.5$	78. $2.61 \times 0.7 \times 0.3$
79. $47.4 \times 0.4 \times 0.9$	80. $61.2 \times 0.12 \times 0.8$.

DIVISION

SHORT DIVISION

EXAMPLE 12   Divide 30.08 by 8.

(Rough answer $30 \div 8 \approx 4$.)

8)30.08
 3.76

$\therefore$ $30.08 \div 8 = 3.76$

EXAMPLE 13   Divide 90.72 by 7.

(Rough answer $90 \div 7 \approx 13$.)

7)90.72
 12.96

$\therefore$ $90.72 \div 7 = 12.96$

EXERCISE 22

Find:

1. $5.28 \div 4$
2. $7.35 \div 5$
3. $14.24 \div 8$
4. $213.6 \div 6$
5. $35.98 \div 7$
6. $54.68 \div 2$
7. $23.79 \div 3$
8. $38.43 \div 9$
9. $5 \div 4$
10. $4 \div 5$
11. $3 \div 5$
12. $5 \div 3$
13. $0.964 \div 2$
14. $0.636 \div 3$
15. $0.918 \div 6$
16. $0.944 \div 8$
17. $0.093 \div 3$
18. $0.168 \div 4$
19. $0.124 \div 8$
20. $0.049 \div 5$
21. $11 \div 5$
22. $15 \div 4$
23. $9 \div 4$
24. $11 \div 8$
25. $3 \div 8$
26. $31 \div 5$
27. $7 \div 8$
28. $15 \div 6$
29. $27 \div 4$
30. $14 \div 4$
31. $43 \div 5$
32. $17 \div 8$
33. $33.04 \div 7$
34. $35.55 \div 9$
35. $25.413 \div 3$
36. $31.52 \div 5$
37. $0.0372 \div 4$
38. $0.1512 \div 7$
39. $0.005\,872 \div 8$
40. $0.2655 \div 9$.

LONG DIVISION

The most common approach to the long division of decimals is to make the divisor (the decimal on the bottom) a whole number.

EXAMPLE 14   Divide 22.386 by 3.64.

(Rough answer $24 \div 4 = 6$.)

$$\frac{22.386}{3.64} = \frac{2238.6}{364}$$ (we have multiplied the numerator and denominator by 100)

```
        6.15
364)2238.6
    2184
     546
     364
    1820
    1820
     . . .
```

∴ $22.386 \div 3.64 = 6.15$

EXAMPLE 15   Divide 42.054 by 0.815.

(Rough answer $42 \div 0.8 = 420 \div 8 \approx 52$.)

$$\frac{42.054}{0.815} = \frac{42\,054}{815}$$ (we have multiplied the top and the bottom by 1000)

```
         51.6
815)42 054.
    4075
    1304
     815
    4890
    4890
     . . .
```

∴ $42.054 \div 0.815 = 51.6$

EXERCISE 23

Find:

1. $35.49 \div 13$ 2. $29.44 \div 16$

3. $118.23 \div 21$ 4. $310.8 \div 37$

5. $202.86 \div 63$ 6. $130.08 \div 24$

7. $17.01 \div 2.7$ 8. $31.05 \div 6.9$

9. $54.76 \div 7.4$ 10. $28.38 \div 3.3$

11. $67.24 \div 8.2$ 12. $56.32 \div 6.4$

13. $964.8 \div 134$ 14. $955.5 \div 735$

15. $2820.7 \div 421$ 16. $14.98 \div 0.7$

17. $49.322 \div 0.91$ 18. $110.51 \div 0.43$

19. $0.231 \div 0.525$ 20. $0.3991 \div 0.614$

21. $0.8507 \div 0.905$ 22. $4.29 \div 0.066$

23. $4.6434 \div 0.071$ 24. $8.256 \div 0.048$

25. $629.67 \div 83.4$ 26. $14.8836 \div 4.74$

27. $1.942\,08 \div 0.476$ 28. $23.1504 \div 4.134$

29. $287.7135 \div 97.53$ 30. $9885.7 \div 163.4$

31. $177.48 \div 48$ 32. $535.5 \div 15.3$

33. $2130.6 \div 40.2$ 34. $10\,122 \div 241$

35. $6411.6 \div 93.6.$

DECIMAL PLACES, NEAREST WHOLE NUMBER, ETC.

It must not be assumed that one decimal will always divide exactly into another.

EXAMPLE 16   Consider $324.6 \div 16.7$.

$$\frac{324.6}{16.7} = \frac{3246}{167}$$

(multiply the top and bottom by 10 to make the denominator a whole number)

```
            19.437 ...
   167)3246.
       167
       ‾‾‾‾
      1576
      1503
      ‾‾‾‾
       730
       668
       ‾‾‾
       620
       501
       ‾‾‾
      1190
      1169
      ‾‾‾‾
        21
```

The difference between 19.44 and 19.437 is 0.003, while the difference between 19.43 and 19.437 is 0.007, i.e. 19.44 is nearer to 19.437 than 19.43 is to it. We say that 19.437 ... correct to two decimal places is 19.44.

Correct to two decimal places means correct to the second figure after the decimal point. This is determined by looking at the number in the third decimal place — if this number is 5 or greater than 5, the number in the second place is increased by 1; if the number in the third place is less than 5, the number in the second place is the number already there.

Example 17 shows numbers correct to two decimal places:

EXAMPLE 17　　(a)　14.943　　　14.94

(b)　39.456　　　39.46

(c)　227.004　　227.00

(d)　79.996　　　80.00

Similarly:

EXAMPLE 18　　(a)　92.75 correct to one decimal place is 92.8.

(b)　0.9247 correct to three decimal places is 0.925.

In a similar way Example 19 gives numbers correct to the nearest whole number, the nearest ten and the nearest hundred.

EXAMPLE 19　　(a)　15.72 correct to the nearest whole number is 16.

(b)　539.73 correct to the nearest ten is 540.

(c)　539.73 correct to the nearest hundred is 500.

EXERCISE 24

Give the following correct to one decimal place:

1.　14.37	2.　39.45	3.　8.927	4.　12.924
5.　3.427	6.　294.95	7.　1027.64	8.　54.99
9.　7.646	10.　73.921	11.　0.934	12.　0.276
13.　0.3727	14.　0.5927	15.　0.8747	16.　0.092
17.　0.076	18.　92.637	19.　61.05	20.　40.08.

Give the following correct to two decimal places:

21.　14.274	22.　50.097	23.　37.345	24.　9.293

25. 7.666	26. 70.249	27. 63.597	28. 42.564	Decimals
29. 8.257	30. 3.495	31. 0.926	32. 0.998	
33. 0.678	34. 0.345	35. 0.143	36. 0.6235	
37. 0.4218	38. 0.7374	39. 0.8264	40. 0.1937.	

Give the following correct to the nearest whole number:

41. 4.274	42. 3.923	43. 16.45	44. 27.64
45. 35.55	46. 19.28	47. 53.47	48. 41.82
49. 73.44	50. 127.74	51. 231.92	52. 527.64
53. 413.9	54. 300.27	55. 404.58	56. 0.927
57. 0.88	58. 8.74	59. 7.39	60. 713.98.

Give the following correct to the nearest ten:

61. 74.9	62. 35.46	63. 216.4	64. 593.7
65. 168.2	66. 824	67. 936	68. 224
69. 523	70. 6844	71. 55.46	72. 14.9
73. 9.267	74. 19.94	75. 73.94	76. 5643
77. 4978	78. 7999	79. 61.94	80. 47.27.

Give the following correct to the nearest hundred:

81. 7420	82. 6180	83. 198.2	84. 589.4
85. 442.4	86. 76.6	87. 3424	88. 1760
89. 59.2	90. 727.9	91. 5379	92. 1264
93. 33 994	94. 56 375	95. 673 492	96. 394.2
97. 829.7	98. 31 455	99. 83 846	100. 9999.

SIGNIFICANT FIGURES

Many questions ask for the answer correct to a certain number of significant figures. A few examples will indicate exactly what this means. A rule worth remembering is that if the first figure to be discarded is a 5 or a figure greater than 5, the previous figure is increased by 1.

EXAMPLE 20   37.4789 is 37.479 correct to five significant figures

37.48   correct to four significant figures

37.5   correct to three significant figures

37   correct to two significant figures

EXAMPLE 21   0.905 36 is 0.9054 correct to four significant figures
0.905   correct to three significant figures
0.91   correct to two significant figures

EXAMPLE 22   0.007 384 is 0.007 38 correct to three significant figures
0.0074 correct to two significant figures
0.007   correct to the first significant figure

EXERCISE 25

Give the following correct to three significant figures:

1. 327.6	2. 413.4	3. 762.5	4. 843.4
5. 192.6	6. 61.29	7. 80.92	8. 36.66
9. 40.33	10. 59.27	11. 2.341	12. 3.927
13. 5.663	14. 9.887	15. 7.342	16. 0.5555
17. 0.6214	18. 0.7378	19. 0.8115	20. 0.5439
21. 1240	22. 6927	23. 8275	24. 4336
25. 3929	26. 0.064 74	27. 0.029 45	28. 0.085 67
29. 0.059 16	30. 0.022 48	31. 36 495	32. 27 644
33. 813 999	34. 54 737	35. 50 098	36. 5.926 43
37. 16.9115	38. 207.462	39. 62 648	40. 0.554 372
41. 73.6429	42. 192 937	43. 0.009 2745	
44. 5.4474	45. 920 064	46. 0.002 937 4	
47. 0.045 67	48. 604 009	49. 82.916	50. 327.4465.

Give the following correct to two significant figures:

51. 543	52. 731	53. 54.24	54. 16.93
55. 34.74	56. 26 745	57. 9.493	58. 18.45
59. 392.61	60. 4.3343	61. 0.927	62. 0.3924
63. 0.7261	64. 0.009 45	65. 0.037 45	66. 204.04
67. 16.09	68. 9.009	69. 8.249	70. 54 643.

Give the following correct to four significant figures:

71. 52 734   72. 17 424   73. 39 245   74. 724.96

75. 362.98   76. 44.246   77. 32.937   78. 3.141 59

79. 2.9876   80. 0.643 21   81. 0.567 89   82. 0.028 673

83. 8.6248   84. 37.1423   85. 98.9481   86. 23.564

87. 0.045 937   88. 473 790   89. 83.456   90. 0.354 28.

Give the following numbers correct to
(a) the nearest whole number
(b) three significant figures
(c) two decimal places:

91. 74.6243   92. 18.5437   93. 24.927   94. 524.147

95. 618.332   96. 828.186   97. 7.924   98. 42.434

99. 8.547   100. 364.624.

EXAMPLE 23   Find $354.3 \div 19.2$ giving your answer

(a) correct to two decimal places
(b) correct to three significant figures.

(Rough answer $350 \div 20 = 17.5$.)

$$\frac{354.3}{19.2} = \frac{3543}{192}$$

```
        18.453       (to obtain the answer correct
192)3543.            to 2 decimal places we find
    192              the quotient to 3 decimal
    1623             places)
    1536
     870
     768
    1020
     960
     600
     576
      24
```

∴ $354.3 \div 19.2$ = 18.45 correct to two decimal
                              places

              = 18.5 correct to three significant
                              figures

55

EXERCISE 26

Evaluate the following correct to two decimal places:

1.	$20.4 \div 8.3$	2.	$37.2 \div 5.7$
3.	$75.4 \div 9.2$	4.	$48.2 \div 4.9$
5.	$13.7 \div 2.6$	6.	$61.4 \div 7.2$
7.	$50.1 \div 5.3$	8.	$89.2 \div 137$
9.	$4.21 \div 17.3$	10.	$0.93 \div 1.8$
11.	$0.41 \div 2.6$	12.	$0.93 \div 0.17$
13.	$723.4 \div 93.6$	14.	$241.2 \div 64.3$
15.	$556.9 \div 327.1$	16.	$0.937 \div 26.4$
17.	$0.873 \div 0.047$	18.	$0.293 \div 0.074$
19.	$654.1 \div 926.2$	20.	$0.573 \div 31.3.$

Evaluate the following correct to three decimal places:

21.	$52.4 \div 49.2$	22.	$73.6 \div 94.2$
23.	$18.92 \div 9.47$	24.	$92.4 \div 137$
25.	$42.7 \div 60.2$	26.	$5.36 \div 10.9$
27.	$0.541 \div 0.23$	28.	$0.643 \div 0.55$
29.	$0.734 \div 0.452$	30.	$0.731 \div 1.84$
31.	$0.848 \div 9.21$	32.	$0.378 \div 21.4$
33.	$592.3 \div 347.8$	34.	$754.3 \div 864$
35.	$6142 \div 839.$		

Evaluate the following correct to three significant figures:

36.	$243 \div 62.4$	37.	$9.87 \div 2.34$
38.	$536.4 \div 337.2$	39.	$6.351 \div 4.92$
40.	$18.36 \div 46.2$	41.	$87.14 \div 236.1$
42.	$0.145 \div 7.35$	43.	$0.44 \div 26.3$
44.	$0.92 \div 62.1$	45.	$40.1 \div 0.076$
46.	$237 \div 0.36$	47.	$884.2 \div 0.093$
48.	$3.21 \div 0.004\,34$	49.	$16.3 \div 0.0876$
50.	$536.1 \div 0.0924.$		

STANDARD FORM

When a number is expressed in the form $a \times 10^n$, where a is a number between 1 and 10 and n is zero or an integer, the number is said to be in *standard form*.

EXAMPLE 24   Express each of the following in standard form:
(a) 512.3, (b) 42.6, (c) 702 000, (d) 0.75,
(e) 0.000 432.

(a) $512.3 = 5.123 \times 100 = 5.123 \times 10^2$

(b) $42.64 = 4.264 \times 10^1$

(c) $702\,000 = 7.02 \times 100\,000 = 7.02 \times 10^5$

(d) $0.75 = \dfrac{7.5}{10} = 7.5 \times 10^{-1}$

(e) $0.000\,432 = \dfrac{4.32}{10\,000} = \dfrac{4.32}{10^4} = 4.32 \times 10^{-4}$

EXERCISE 27

Express each of the following in standard form:

1. 72.6
2. 183.4
3. 5000
4. 424.2

5. 82 400
6. 1 230 000
7. 0.5
8. 0.43

9. 0.842
10. 0.07
11. 0.009
12. 0.0412

13. 0.0093
14. 0.000 02
15. 0.000 054 3.

16. If $a = 1.2 \times 10^4$ and $b = 3 \times 10^2$, find (i) $a + b$, (ii) ab, (iii) $a \div b$, expressing each answer in standard form.

17. If $a = 5 \times 10^4$ and $b = 25 \times 10^3$, find (i) $a + b$, (ii) ab, (iii) $a \div b$, (iv) $b \div a$, giving each answer in standard form.

18. If $a = 3.6 \times 10^4$ and $b = 4 \times 10^{-3}$, find (i) ab, (ii) $a \div b$, expressing each answer in standard form.

19. If $a = 4.2 \times 10^{-3}$ and $b = 6 \times 10^{-5}$, find (i) $a + b$, (ii) $a - b$, (iii) ab, (iv) $a \div b$, expressing each answer in standard form.

20. If $a = 8.4 \times 10^{-5}$ and $b = 2.1 \times 10^6$, find (i) ab, (ii) $a \div b$, expressing each answer in standard form.

5

DIRECTED NUMBERS

ADDITION AND SUBTRACTION

We are all familiar with the temperatures given on the TV weather charts for different parts of the country at different times of the year. During the summer, temperatures everywhere are + numbers, but in the winter we frequently see − numbers. On the centigrade scale the temperature at which water freezes is marked $0°$. Temperatures above this are referred to as + temperatures, and those below as − temperatures. If the temperature was $8°$ at 8 a.m. but $11°$ at noon, it would have risen by $3°$. We denote rising by $3°$ as $+3°$, therefore $8°$ plus $(+3°) = 11°$.

If the temperature at 6 p.m. on the same day is $6°$, it has fallen by $5°$, and we denote this fall by $-5°$, i.e. $11°$ plus $(-5°) = 6°$.

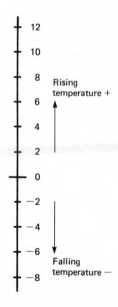

If the initial temperature is $4°$ and it falls $6°$, then the thermometer reads $-2°$

i.e. $\qquad 4°$ plus $(-6°) = -2°$

If the initial temperature is $-2°$ and it falls $5°$, then the thermometer reads $-7°$

i.e. $\qquad -2°$ plus $(-5°) = -7°$

Numbers such as $+3$ and -7 are called *directed numbers*. The $-$ sign therefore means 'in the opposite direction to $+$'.

In this context we can therefore say that:

(a) a loss of £10 is the same as a profit of $-$£10,

(b) -15 minutes late is the same as 15 minutes early,

(c) -40 metres above ground is the same as 40 metres below ground,

(d) paying £100 into the bank is the same as withdrawing $-$£100 from it.

EXERCISE 28

Give alternative statements for each of the following:

1. The clock is -3 minutes fast.

2. The clock is 5 minutes slow.

3. I pay $-$£20 into my bank account.

4. I withdraw $-$£50 from my bank account.

5. Peter climbs -100 metres up a mountain.

6. Jane walks down 6 stairs.

7. -50 litres of water flows into the bath.

8. Tom walks -3 kilometres due south.

9. Mary receives a pay rise of -6%.

10. The price of gold decreases by 20%.

11. The population of Eastmouth increases by -2000.

12. Bolton beat Hyde by -2 goals.

We are therefore able to conclude that a rise of -2 is the same as a fall of 2, and that a fall of -2 is the same as a rise of 2. Denoting a rise by $+$ and a fall by $-$ we can therefore write:

$$+(-2) = -2$$

and $\qquad -(-2) = +2$

EXAMPLE 1   (a) $5 + (-2) = 5 - 2 = 3$
(b) $-5 + (-2) = -5 - 2 = -7$
(c) $8 - (-2) = 8 + 2 = 10$
(d) $-8 - (-3) = -8 + 3 = -5$

EXAMPLE 2   (a) Add -2 to 8.
$$8 + (-2) = 8 - 2 = 6$$

(b) Add -4 to -7.
$$-7 + (-4) = -7 - 4 = -11$$

(c) Subtract -3 from 12.
$$12 - (-3) = 12 + 3 = 15$$

(d) Subtract -7 from -9.
$$-9 - (-7) = -9 + 7 = -2$$

EXAMPLE 3   Simplify:
(a) $8 - 2 - 10 = 8 - 12 = -4$
(b) $7 - (5 - 2) = 7 - 3 = 4$
(c) $-10 + (3 - 7) - 4 = -10 + (-4) - 4$
$$= -10 - 4 - 4 = -18$$

EXERCISE 29

Simplify:

1. $10 + (-5)$ 2. $7 + (-3)$
3. $12 + (-9)$ 4. $20 + (-17)$
5. $8 + (-10)$ 6. $6 + (-14)$
7. $10 + (-20)$ 8. $15 + (-21)$
9. $(-4) + (-3)$ 10. $(-10) + (-2)$
11. $(-8) + (-5)$ 12. $(-14) + (-16)$
13. $(15) - (-2)$ 14. $(16) - (-8)$
15. $(-14) - (-3)$ 16. $(-8) - (-12)$
17. $10 - (-5)$ 18. $(-16) - (-4)$
19. $(-9) - (-7)$ 20. $(-18) + (-7)$
21. $5 + (-3) + (-2)$ 22. $12 + (-6) + (-4)$
23. $8 + (-5) + (-3)$ 24. $12 + (-8) + (-6)$
25. $9 - (-4) + (-5)$ 26. $6 + (-3) - (-8)$
27. $4 - (-2) + (-3)$ 28. $10 + (-5) - (-5)$

29. $(-8)+(-4)+(-2)$
30. $(-5)+(-3)+(-7)$
31. $(-12)-(-2)+(-8)$
32. $(-5)+(-6)-(-4)$
33. $(-7)-(-8)+(-4)$
34. $(-10)+(-8)-(-3)$
35. $-(-3)+(-2)+(-4)$
36. $-(-5)+(-6)$
37. $-(-8)-(-4)+(-2)$
38. $-(-10)-(-6)+(-5)$
39. $-(-7)+(-2)-(-6)$
40. $-(-9)+(-7)-(-5)$

MULTIPLICATION AND DIVISION

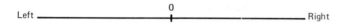

Imagine a boy walking along the half-way line on a football pitch. Suppose he walks at 2 metres per second (m/s) and starts walking on the hour.

A speed of $+2$ m/s means that he walks to the right, while a speed of -2 m/s means that he walks to the left. Similarly for time: $+5$ seconds means 5 seconds after the hour, and -5 seconds means 5 seconds before the hour.

If he walks from the centre 0 for $+5$ seconds at a speed of $+2$ m/s where is he?

$$10 \text{ metres to the right of } 0 \text{ or } (+5)\times(+2) = +10 \text{ m}$$

If he walks from the centre for $+5$ seconds at a speed of -2 m/s where is he?

$$10 \text{ metres to the left of } 0 \text{ or } (+5)\times(-2) = -10 \text{ m}$$

If he walks from the centre for -5 seconds at a speed of 2 m/s where is he?

$$10 \text{ metres to the left of } 0 \text{ or } (-5)\times(+2) = -10 \text{ m}$$

If he walks from the centre for -5 seconds at a speed of -2 m/s where is he?

$$10 \text{ metres to the right of } 0 \text{ or } (-5)\times(-2) = +10 \text{ m}$$

If he is at 0 at time 0 seconds, then 5 seconds previous to this (i.e. at -5 seconds) he was 10 metres to the right of 0).

The above four results enable us to formulate the rule that: like signs *multiplied together* give a plus sign while unlike signs *multiplied together* give a minus sign.

It follows that if $(-5)\times(-2) = +10$

then $(+10)\div(-2) = -5$

61

Similarly since $(+5)\times(-2)=-10$

$$(-10)\div(-2)\ =\ 5$$

Hence: division of like signs gives a plus sign while division of unlike signs gives a minus sign.

EXAMPLE 4   (a) $(+10)\times(-6)=-60$
   (b) $(-24)\times(+3)=-72$
   (c) $(-6)\times(-5)=+30$

EXAMPLE 5   (a) $(-20)\div4=-5$
   (b) $(30)\div(-6)=-5$
   (c) $(-24)\div(-4)=6$

EXAMPLE 6   (a) $(-5)\times(4)\times(-3)=(-20)\times(-3)=60$

   (b) $\dfrac{(-6)\times4}{(-12)}=\dfrac{(-24)}{(-12)}=2$

   (c) $(-8\div4)\times(-2)=(-2)\times(-2)=4$

   (d) $(-4)^3\div16=\dfrac{(-4)\times(-4)\times(-4)}{16}=\dfrac{-64}{16}=-4$

EXERCISE 30

Simplify:

1. $4\times(-3)$	2. $(-4)\times2$	3. $(-5)\times(-4)$
4. $(-14)\times3$	5. $-(14\times3)$	6. $14\times(-5)$
7. $(-13)\times(-3)$	8. $(-5)\times3$	9. $(-12)\div12$
10. $12\div(-3)$	11. $(-24)\div3$	12. $(-36)\div(-12)$
13. $8\div(-4)$	14. $(-16)\div4$	15. $(-27)\div(-9)$
16. $(-15)\div(-5)$	17. $\dfrac{99}{-11}$	18. $\dfrac{-88}{11}$
19. $\dfrac{-55}{-5}$	20. $\dfrac{16}{-4}$	21. $\dfrac{-28}{7}$
22. $\dfrac{-16}{-8}$	23. $\dfrac{24}{-3}$	24. $\dfrac{-48}{-24}$
25. $\dfrac{-14}{7}$	26. $\dfrac{24}{-8}$	27. $\dfrac{-144}{-16}$
28. $\dfrac{-9}{-27}$	29. $3(4-2)$	30. $5(-3-4)$

31. $6(-7+9)$

32. $5(-3+4)$

33. $-3(7-2)$

34. $-8(-5+4)$

35. $-6(-6-2)$

36. $-6(-8-1)$

37. $\dfrac{9-3}{3}$

38. $\dfrac{-17-8}{5}$

39. $\dfrac{-5-7}{4}$

40. $\dfrac{-28-8}{12}$

41. $\dfrac{21-3}{-6}$

42. $\dfrac{-9-7}{-8}$

43. $\dfrac{-19+7}{-2}$

44. $\dfrac{-31-19}{-10}$

45. $(8-4)\times2$

46. $(8-4)\div2$

47. $8\div(4-2)$

48. $8\div(-4+2)$

49. $(8\div4)-2$

50. $8\times(4\times2)$

51. $8\times4\times(-2)$

52. $8\times(-4)\times2$

53. $8\times(-4)\times(-2)$

54. $(8\div4)\times2$

55. $(8\div4)\times(-2)$

56. $(8\div4)\times4$

57. $(-8\div4)\times2$

58. $(-8\div4)-2$

59. $(-8\div4)+2$

60. $8\div(4\div2)$

61. $8-(4\div2)$

62. $8\div(4-2)$

63. $8\div(4\times2)$

64. $8\div(-4\times2)$

65. $8+(-4\div2)$

66. $(8+4)\div(-2)$

67. $4\div(8\times2)$

68. $(-4\div8)\times2$

69. $\dfrac{(-3)\times(-4)\times(-5)}{-60}$

70. $\dfrac{(-1)\times4\times(-6)}{-36}$

71. $\dfrac{(-3)^2\times(-4)}{12}$

72. $(-3)^2\times(-2)^3$

73. $\dfrac{(-4)^2\times(-3)}{2(-6-2)}$

74. $\dfrac{8\times(-4)\times(-2)^2}{(-12)\times(-2)}$

75. $\dfrac{(-12)\times(-4)}{12\div(-4)}$.

THE METRIC SYSTEM

The metric system of units is a simplified version of a system of weights and measures which was introduced in France in 1790 during the French Revolution. It is essentially a decimal system, the standard unit of length being the metre (m) and the standard unit of mass being the kilogram (kg), although the gram (g) is frequently used.

The metre was intended to be one ten-millionth of the distance from the equator to the North Pole as measured along the line of longitude through Paris. Its exact value is now defined by reference to a particular wavelength of electromagnetic radiation.

The same prefixes occur several times in the metric system, and outside it. It is therefore important to learn these: *kilo* means thousand, *centi* means one hundredth and *milli* means one thousandth.

LENGTH

The basic unit of length is the *metre*. A length of one thousand metres is called a *kilometre*. The metre may be divided into one hundred equal parts each of which is called a *centimetre*. It may also be divided into one thousand equal parts each of which is called a *millimetre*.

Hence

$$1 \text{ kilometre (km)} = 1000 \text{ metres (m)}$$

$$1 \text{ centimetre (cm)} = \frac{1}{100} \text{ metre (m)}$$

$$1 \text{ millimetre (mm)} = \frac{1}{1000} \text{ metre (m)}$$

It follows that:

$$1 \text{ km } = 1000 \text{ m}$$
$$100 \text{ cm } = 1 \text{ m}$$
$$1000 \text{ mm } = 1 \text{ m}$$

and

$$10 \text{ mm } = 1 \text{ cm}$$

EXAMPLE 1   Convert 5.264 m into (a) centimetres, (b) milli-metres.

$$5.264 \text{ m } = 5.264 \times 100 \text{ cm } = 526.4 \text{ cm}$$
$$5.264 \text{ m } = 5.264 \times 1000 \text{ m } = 5264 \text{ mm}$$

EXAMPLE 2   Convert 0.458 km into metres.

$$0.458 \text{ km } = 0.458 \times 1000 \text{ m } = 458 \text{ m}$$

EXAMPLE 3   Express (a) 5 cm 4 mm in millimetres, (b) 3 m 84 cm 5 mm in centimetres.

(a) 5 cm 4 mm $= 50 \text{ mm} + 4 \text{ mm} = 54 \text{ mm}$
(b) 3 m 84 cm 5 mm $= 300 \text{ cm} + 84 \text{ cm} + 0.5 \text{ cm}$
     $= 384.5 \text{ cm}$

When adding or subtracting metric quantities it is important that all quantities are converted into a common unit.

EXAMPLE 4   Add 2 m 37 cm, 84 cm and 534 mm giving your answer in (a) millimetres, (b) metres.

(a) 2 m 37 cm $= 2370 \text{ mm}$
     84 cm $= 840 \text{ mm}$
     534 mm $= 534 \text{ mm}$
     $\therefore$ Sum $= 3744 \text{ mm}$

(b) 3744 mm $= 3.744 \text{ m}$

EXAMPLE 5   Subtract 434 m 84 cm from 2 km. Give your answer in metres.

     2 km $= 2000 \quad \text{m}$
     434 m 84 cm $= 434.84 \text{ m}$
     $\therefore$ Difference $= 1565.16 \text{ m}$

EXAMPLE 6   From a ball of string 50 m long one hundred and five lengths, each 45 cm, are cut. What length of string remains?

Total length of 105 pieces each of length 45 cm
= 105 × 45 cm = 4725 cm.

Original length of ball = 50 m = 5000 cm.

∴ Amount remaining = (5000 − 4725) cm

= 275 cm

EXERCISE 31

1. Measure each of the following straight lines correct to the nearest centimetre:
   (a) _____
   (b) _____
   (c) _____
   (d) _____

2. Measure each of the following straight lines correct to the nearest millimetre:
   (a) _____
   (b) _____
   (c) _____
   (d) _____

3. Measure each of the following straight lines in (i) centimetres, (ii) millimetres:
   (a) _____
   (b) _____
   (c) _____
   (d) _____

4. Draw straight lines of the following lengths:
   (a) 3 cm   (b) 7 cm   (c) 12 cm   (d) 9.5 cm.

5. Draw straight lines of the following lengths:
   (a) 35 mm   (b) 82 mm   (c) 58 mm   (d) 26 mm.

6. Which metric unit would it be most sensible to use to measure:
   (a) the width of the nearest road
   (b) your height
   (c) the height of a lamp standard
   (d) the distance between Paris and Rome
   (e) the thickness of a piece of window glass.

7. Convert into metres:
   (a) 12 km   (b) 4.32 km   (c) 0.68 km   (d) 529 cm
   (e) 4360 cm   (f) 26 cm   (g) 734 mm   (h) 38 mm
   (i) 60.24 km   (j) 49.7 cm.

8. Convert into centimetres:
   (a) 24 m   (b) 3.6 m   (c) 0.49 m   (d) 0.026 m
   (e) 44 mm   (f) 634 mm   (g) 7.31 mm   (h) 0.04 mm
   (i) 1.732 km   (j) 0.0264 km.

9. Convert into millimetres:
  (a) 37 cm   (b) 13.5 cm   (c) 9.12 cm   (d) 0.46 cm
  (e) 8.4 m   (f) 27 m   (g) 0.73 m   (h) 0.024 m
  (i) 1.243 km   (j) 0.092 km.

10. Convert into kilometres:
  (a) 5000 m   (b) 10 000 m   (c) 750 m   (d) 4360 m
  (e) 830 m   (f) 17 630 cm   (g) 49 360 cm
  (h) 763 cm   (i) 143 400 mm
  (j) 7 230 000 mm.

11. Add the following, giving each answer in metres:
  (a) 3 m, 42 cm, 1 m 50 cm, 8 m 74 cm
  (b) 59 cm, 84 cm, 2430 mm
  (c) 643 cm, 842 mm, 3914 mm
  (d) 2.1 km, 904 m, 8640 cm
  (e) 0.04 km, 53 m, 892 m.

12. Subtract the second length from the first, giving your answer in
    metres:
  (a) 12 m, 200 cm   (b) 34 m, 14.3 m
  (c) 60 m, 4930 cm   (d) 45.2 cm, 164 mm
  (e) 2934 mm, 1.36 m.

13. Express the following as mixed quantities in terms of metres,
    centimetres and millimetres:
  (a) 30.24 m   (b) 2436 cm   (c) 7490 mm   (d) 0.024 16 km
  (e) 92 600 mm   (f) 6724 cm   (g) 10 304 cm.

14. Find the following giving each answer in metres:
  (a) 4 m − 264 cm + 930 mm
  (b) 7.2 m − 437 cm + 2600 mm
  (c) 826 cm − 2.45 m + 200 mm
  (d) 1400 cm − 3940 mm − 8.36 m
  (e) 2640 mm + 0.92 m − 356 cm.

15. The diameter of a penny is 2 cm. How many pennies placed side
    by side will extend a distance of 5 m?

16. A 2p coin has a diameter of 2.5 cm. How many 2p coins placed
    side by side are required to extend a distance of 100 m?

17. How many pencils of length 18 cm, placed end to end, are required
    to stretch 100 m?

18. How many concrete blocks, each 22 cm high, are required to reach
    a height of 1.76 m?

19. How many concrete blocks, each 60 cm long, are required to build
    one course of a wall 33.6 m long?

20. A book is 6.6 mm thick. How many similar books may be stored
    on a shelf 1.65 m long?

MASS

The basic unit of mass is the kilogram (kg), which is defined from a standard block of metal kept near Paris.

$$1 \text{ kilogram (kg)} = 1000 \text{ grams (g)}$$

and $\qquad 1 \text{ milligram (mg)} = \dfrac{1}{1000} \text{ gram (g)} = \dfrac{1}{1\,000\,000} \text{kg}$

For large masses we use the metric tonne (t) where 1 tonne = 1000 kilograms

∴ $\qquad\qquad 1 \text{ kg} = 1000 \text{ g}$

$\qquad\qquad\qquad 1 \text{ g} = 1000 \text{ mg}$

and $\qquad\qquad 1 \text{ t} = 1000 \text{ kg}$

EXAMPLE 7 Convert:
  (a) 1.93 kg into grams
  (b) 0.043 t into kilograms
  (c) 73 400 mg into grams
  (d) 59 300 g into kilograms

(a) Since $\quad 1 \text{ kg} = 1000 \text{ g}$

$\qquad 1.93 \text{ kg} = 1.93 \times 1000 \text{ g} = 1930 \text{ g}$

(b) Since $\quad 1 \text{ t} = 1000 \text{ kg}$

$\qquad 0.043 \text{ t} = 0.043 \times 1000 \text{ kg} = 43 \text{ kg}$

(c) Since $\quad 1000 \text{ mg} = 1 \text{ g}$

$\qquad 73\,400 \text{ mg} = \dfrac{73\,400}{1000} \text{ g} = 73.4 \text{ g}$

(d) Since $\quad 1000 \text{ g} = 1 \text{ kg}$

$\qquad 59\,300 \text{ g} = \dfrac{59\,300}{1000} \text{ kg} = 59.3 \text{ kg}$

EXAMPLE 8 Add 5.43 kg, 8460 g, 293 400 mg and 0.0443 t, giving your answer in kilograms.

$$5.43 \text{ kg} = 5.43 \text{ kg}$$
$$8640 \text{ g} = 8.64 \text{ kg}$$
$$293\,400 \text{ mg} = 0.2934 \text{ kg}$$
$$0.0443 \text{ t} = 44.3 \text{ kg}$$

∴ Total mass = 58.6634 kg

EXAMPLE 9   Express 54 346 g in terms of kilograms and grams.

$$54\,346\,g \;=\; 54\,000\,g + 346\,g$$
$$= \; 54\,kg\;346\,g$$

EXAMPLE 10   A van carries a load of 0.5 t which is made up of 30 boxes, each containing 36 tins of cooked meat, together with 2 boxes of fresh fruit each of mass 4.3 kg. Calculate the mass of 1 tin of cooked meat.

Total mass of load $=\; 0.5\,t \;=\; 500\,kg$

Mass of 2 boxes of fruit at 4.3 kg per box $=\; 8.6\,kg$

$\therefore$ Mass of 30 boxes of cooked meat $=\; 491.4\,kg$

$\therefore$ Mass of 1 box of cooked meat $= \dfrac{491.4}{30}$

$$= \; 16.38\,kg$$

i.e.   Mass of 36 tins of cooked meat $=\; 16.38\,kg$

$$= \; 16\,380\,g$$

$\therefore$ Mass of 1 tin of cooked meat $= \dfrac{16\,380}{36}$

$$= \; 455\,g$$

$\therefore$ Each tin has a mass of 455 g

EXERCISE 32   MISCELLANEOUS EXAMPLES

1. What units would you expect to use to measure the mass of each of the following?
    (a)   a car
    (b)   a loaded petrol tanker
    (c)   a saccharin tablet
    (d)   one page from this book
    (e)   a bag of potatoes.

2. Convert into grams:
    (a)   250 mg   (b)   5700 mg   (c)   73 400 mg
    (d)   4730 mg   (e)   5.42 kg   (f)   20.4 kg   (g)   0.73 kg
    (h)   0.0493 kg.

3. Convert into kilograms:
    (a)   7600 g   (b)   491 g   (c)   97.2 g   (d)   6040 g
    (e)   926 400 mg   (f)   55 450 mg
    (g)   374 mg   (h)   8497 mg.

4. Convert into milligrams:
   (a) 54 g   (b) 429 g   (c) 1.24 g   (d) 0.46 g.
   (e) 1.2 kg   (f) 0.044 kg   (g) 0.217 kg   (h) 0.000 84 kg.

5. Convert:
   (a) 3420 kg into tonnes
   (b) 1.74 t into kilograms
   (c) 0.047 t into kilograms
   (d) 83 440 kg into tonnes
   (e) 504 600 kg into tonnes.

6. Add the following masses, giving your answers in kilograms:
   (a) 240 kg, 0.42 t, 34 kg   (b) 3 kg, 864 g, 736 g
   (c) 544 g, 1.24 kg, 64 g   (d) 65 000 mg, 434 g, 0.244 kg
   (e) 0.06 t, 240 kg, 0.416 t.

7. Add the following masses, giving your answers in grams:
   (a) 7340 mg, 25.4 g, 1350 mg   (b) 2.6 g, 0.0042 kg, 55 400 mg
   (c) 270 mg, 16.4 g, 550 mg   (d) 0.074 kg, 8640 mg, 65.5 g.

8. Subtract the first mass from the second, giving your answer in grams:
   (a) 760 g, 1.46 kg   (b) 2.57 kg, 6480 g
   (c) 640 mg, 1.26 g   (d) 1870 mg, 0.004 88 kg
   (e) 0.000 092 kg, 687 mg.

9. Express in mixed quantities in terms of kilograms and grams:
   (a) 9430 g   (b) 1691 g   (c) 3450 g   (d) 13.74 kg
   (e) 28.4 kg.

10. A tin of tomatoes has a mass of 230 g. What is the mass, in kilograms, of a case containing 72 such tins?

11. A jar of marmalade has a mass of 454 g. What is the mass, in kilograms, of a carton containing 48 such jars?

12. If the mass of a 2 p coin is 7.12 g, find the mass in kilograms of a bag containing £20 of such coins.

13. A bag containing penny coins has a mass of 5.34 kg. If each coin has a mass of 3.56 g what is the total value of the coins in the bag?

14. A lorry has an unladen mass of 5 t 40 kg, and carries a load of 180 bags of potatoes, each with mass 25 kg. What is the combined mass, in tonnes, of the lorry plus the potatoes?

15. Into an empty carton of mass 80 g are placed six cakes, each of mass 195 g. Calculate the mass of the carton when full.

16. A tin of fruit cocktail has a mass of 326 g. Find the mass, in kilograms, of a box which contains 36 such tins, allowing 1 kg for the mass of the empty box.

17. A fifty-four-seater coach leaves for a package holiday with every seat taken. If the passengers are of average mass 82 kg and each passenger has 35 kg of luggage, find the total mass of the passengers plus their luggage.

18. Ham is sold in tins, each tin having a mass of 198 g. Find the total mass of a carton containing 72 such tins if the carton has a mass of 550 g.

19. The mass of a can of Bucko corned beef is 340 g. If 48 such cans are packed into a case of mass 600 g, find the mass of 50 full cases.

20. Fifty-four tins of tomato soup are placed in a box of mass 456 g. If the combined mass of tins and box is 24 kg, find the mass, in grams, of one tin of soup.

21. Forty-eight tins of pineapple cubes together with their packaging have a mass of 22 kg. If the mass of the packaging is 928 g, calculate the mass of five tins of pineapple cubes.

22. A housewife returns from the supermarket with:

    6 bags of sugar, each of mass 2.2 kg
    12 cans of beans, each of mass 425 g
    4 packets of cereal, each of mass 440 g and
    8 jars of jam, each of mass 454 g.

    Calculate the total mass of her purchases.

23. A lorry is loaded with:

    64 boxes, each of mass 22 kg
    44 boxes, each of mass 34 kg
    152 boxes, each of mass 18 kg and
    98 boxes, each of mass 26 kg.

    Find the total mass of the load in tonnes.

24. Table salt is sold in boxes of mass 1.5 kg. If a salt cellar requires 35.5 g of salt to fill it, how many times could it be filled from one box of table salt? Give your answer correct to the nearest whole number.

25. An aircraft has 320 seats. If all the seats are occupied with passengers of average mass 78 kg, and each passenger is allowed 20 kg of luggage, calculate the total potential mass of passengers plus their luggage.

REVISION PAPERS

PAPER 1

1. Add 143, 7264, 92 and 736.

2. Multiply 437 by 55.

3. Express 5184 in prime factors and hence find its square root.

4. Reduce $\dfrac{2160}{5040}$ to its lowest terms.

5. How many lengths of cloth, each 3.25 m long may be cut from a 100 m roll? How much is left over?

PAPER 2

1. Subtract 3659 from 5000.

2. Divide 9648 by 72.

3. Express 5733 in prime factors. What is the smallest number by which 5733 must be multiplied to make it a perfect square?

4. Calculate the total mass in kilograms of 84 packets each containing a mass of 476 g.

5. Write down the next two numbers in the sequence 19, 14, 9, ...

PAPER 3

1. Add 2764, 3419, 83 and 9264.

2. A train leaves Manchester at 3.36 p.m. and arrives in London 117 minutes later. Find its time of arrival.

3. Divide fourteen thousand three hundred and thirty-eight by two hundred and fourteen.

4. Express 9261 in prime factors and hence find its cube root.

5. Simplify (a) $\dfrac{5}{8} \times \dfrac{4}{3}$, (b) $\dfrac{7}{8} \div \dfrac{3}{4}$.

PAPER 4

1. Find the sum of all the whole numbers between 16 and 31 which are exactly divisible by 3.

2. Write down the next two terms in the series $8 + 9 + 11 + 14 + \ldots$.

3. Express 630 and 1728 in prime factors. Hence find their HCF and LCM.

4. Simplify (a) $\dfrac{5}{7} + \dfrac{5}{14}$, (b) $\dfrac{5}{7} - \dfrac{5}{14}$.

5. A factory worker, on a five day week, starts work at 7.30 a.m. and works until 4 p.m. with three-quarters of an hour off for lunch. How many hours does he work in a week?

PAPER 5

1. Find $7261 - 4395 + 743 - 1436$.

2. Find the mass, in kilograms, of 34 articles each with mass 127 g. How much more, or less, is this than the mass of 18 articles each with a mass 248 g?

3. Simplify $5\dfrac{1}{4} \times 1\dfrac{7}{9}$.

4. Evaluate (a) 123.5×0.89, (b) $123.5 \div 0.89$, giving each answer correct to one decimal place.

5. Lamp standards, which are set at 50 m intervals along a straight road, are numbered consecutively. If Jane walks from standard number 67 to standard number 127, how far does she walk in kilometres?

PAPER 6

1. Express $375\,\text{m}$ as a fraction of $2\,\text{km}$, giving your answer in its lowest terms.

2. Simplify $5\dfrac{1}{7} \div 1\dfrac{23}{49}$.

3. Simplify (a) $1.24 + 0.36 - 0.84$, (b) 0.8×0.4.

4. A school opens at 8.45 a.m. and closes at 3.35 p.m. The lunch break is from 12.20 p.m. to 1.35 p.m. and there is a 15 minute mid-morning break. How long are the pupils at work in (a) a day, (b) a week, (c) a school year consisting of 195 days?

5. At a local election with three candidates, Mr Brown received $\frac{1}{3}$ of the votes cast, Mrs Collard $\frac{2}{5}$ and Miss Durley $\frac{1}{4}$. If there were 73 spoilt papers, how many people voted and how many votes did the winner receive?

PAPER 7

1. A football supporters' club hires fifty-four-seater coaches to transport 4364 supporters to an away match. How many coaches are required?

2. How much larger is the sum of 842 and 736 than the difference between 1000 and 136?

3. Multiply 924 by 234 and divide the result by 273.

4. Find (a) 1.2×0.7, (b) $0.024 \div 12$.

5. Write down the next three numbers in the sequence 10, 15, 19, 22, ...

PAPER 8

1. The product of three numbers, two of which are 13 and 17, is 4199. Find the third number.

2. The length of a man's pace is 90 cm. How many paces does he take to walk $2\frac{2}{5}$ km?

3. Find (a) 4.2×1.6, (b) $371 \div 0.7$.

4. Twelve cars, each of length $4.72\,\text{m}$, are parked nose to tail with a 65 cm gap between each car and the next. Calculate the total distance from the front of the first to the back of the last.

5. Simplify (a) $8 - 4(-2)$, (b) $-24 \div (-6 + 2)$.

PAPER 9

1. Find the sum of 34.62, 7.09, 0.845 and 40.

2. Subtract the difference between 8950 and 4689 from the sum of 5376 and 1294.

3. Divide 42.64 by 12.3 giving your answer correct to two decimal places.

4. Four auto parts in a set have masses 17.5 g, 21 g, 28 g and 33.5 g. Find the mass, in kilograms, of twelve such sets.

5. In the fourth year of a school $\frac{3}{5}$ of the pupils study geography and $\frac{1}{3}$ of those who do not study geography study history. If 30 fourth formers study neither history nor geography, how many pupils are there in the fourth year?

PAPER 10

1. Simplify $\left(2\frac{1}{4} - 1\frac{1}{3}\right) \div \frac{11}{24}$.

2. Find the quotient and remainder when 7345 is divided by 126.

3. A load of coal was divided between four brothers. The first received $\frac{1}{3}$ of it, the second $\frac{2}{5}$, the third $\frac{1}{7}$ and the fourth 273 kg. Calculate the original mass of coal and the amount received by the first brother.

4. Give 293.746 correct to (a) the nearest hundred, (b) three significant figures, (c) two decimal places.

5. There are 1511 pupils in a school. If there are 43 fewer boys than girls, how many girls are there?

PAPER 11

1. Express 14 896 in prime factors. Hence find the smallest number by which it must be multiplied to make it a perfect square.

2. Express (a) $\frac{73}{36}$ as a decimal, (b) 5.016 as a mixed number in its lowest terms.

3. Multiply 1.732 by 44.6.

4. Simplify (a) $(-14 \div 4) \div 2$, (b) $(-5 \div 10) \times (-2)$.

5. A tennis ball bounces to $\frac{2}{3}$ of the height from which it is dropped. If it is dropped from a height of 6 m, how high will it rise after it has struck the ground for the second time?

PAPER 12

1. Find the sum of all the whole numbers between 24 and 36 which are not multiples of 3.

2. Divide 10.6026 by 0.431.

3. Evaluate $404 \div 63.2$ correct to two decimal places.

4. Find the HCF of 5100 and 2100 giving your answer as the product of prime factors.

5. Simplify $1\frac{1}{3} \times 1\frac{8}{9} \div 3\frac{7}{9}$.

PAPER 13

1. Find $\frac{3}{7}$ of 393.4 m.

2. Write down the next two numbers in the series $7 + 23 + 48 + 84 + \ldots$.

3. Express (a) 0.775, (b) 0.268, as common fractions in their lowest terms.

4. Evaluate $926.43 \div 154.2$ correct to two decimal places.

5. Mr Ali buys a new car which it is claimed should give 42 miles per gallon. He finds it gives 38 miles per gallon. How much extra petrol will he require in a year when he travels 11 172 miles?

PAPER 14

1. Express 70.748 correct to (a) the nearest whole number, (b) two decimal places, (c) three significant figures.

2. Simplify (a) $\dfrac{7.2 \times 0.4}{36}$, (b) $0.3 \times 0.3 \times 0.3$.

3. Simplify $\left(4\frac{1}{3} - 2\frac{2}{7}\right) \times \dfrac{49}{86}$.

4. A lorry is loaded with 84 cases each of mass 112 kg. If the mass of the lorry when loaded is 13 908 kg, calculate its unladen mass.

5. A bag of marbles is divided between three boys. Kevin had $\frac{1}{6}$ of them, Brian twice as many as Kevin, and Donald had 84. How many does Brian have?

PAPER 15

1. Express 5880 as the product of prime numbers. Hence determine whether or not 5880 is exactly divisible by 105.

2. Patsy Kagan uses the train to go to work taking 55 seconds for each mile. Her train journey is 26 miles each way. Calculate the total time she spends on the train each week if she works a $5\frac{1}{2}$ day week.

3. Arrange $\dfrac{5}{13}, \dfrac{7}{15}, \dfrac{4}{7}$ in ascending order.

4. Simplify (a) 0.043×8.06, (b) $11.6232 \div 0.348$.

5. A greengrocer bought 207 oranges and found that $\frac{1}{9}$ were bad. How many were fit to eat?

PAPER 16

1. Express 493.078 correct to (a) the nearest 10, (b) three significant figures, (c) one decimal place.

2. Write down the next two terms in the sequence $\dfrac{7}{8}, \dfrac{8}{9}, \dfrac{9}{10}, \ldots$.

3. Arrange $\dfrac{9}{20}, \dfrac{11}{24}, \dfrac{9}{16}$ in descending order.

4. If 2.54 cm equals 1 inch and 12 inches equals one foot, express 100 m in feet correct to two decimal places.

5. How many hours will it take a train to travel 420 km at 175 km per hour?

PAPER 17

1. Multiply 2.64 by 0.492. Give your answer correct to (a) three significant figures, (b) three decimal places.

2. By what must $3\dfrac{4}{7}$ be multiplied to make $\dfrac{2}{5}$?

3. Simplify $\left(1\dfrac{3}{8}+2\dfrac{3}{4}\right)-\left(\dfrac{1}{3}+\dfrac{5}{6}\right)$.

4. Express 0.906 25 as a common fraction in its lowest terms.

5. A man walks 144 miles in 4 days by walking for 12 hours each day. How many days will he take to cover 216 miles walking for 9 hours a day if he walks at the same rate?

PAPER 18

1. Simplify $5\dfrac{3}{7}\times 7-12\dfrac{4}{5}$.

2. Calculate $(45-3\times 13)\div(-2)$.

3. Express $2\dfrac{2}{21}$ as a decimal.

4. How long is the sun up if it rises at 4.45 a.m. and sets at 7.12 p.m.?

5. A retailer buys a quantity of apples. $\frac{2}{7}$ were sold on Thursday, $\frac{3}{8}$ on Friday and $\frac{1}{5}$ on Saturday. If 156 apples remain unsold, how many were sold on Friday?

PAPER 19

1. Calculate (a) 4.8×0.9, (b) $4.8\div 0.9$, (c) $4.8-0.9$.

2. Express 3600 as a product of prime numbers in index form and hence find its square root.

3. Express 67.459 correct to (a) the nearest whole number, (b) one decimal place, (c) four significant figures.

4. The government increased the price of petrol by $\frac{1}{5}$ and the following year increased the new price by a further $\frac{1}{5}$. By what fraction has the original price been increased to give the final price?

5. Allowing 2 mm for each saw cut, how many pieces, each 54 cm long, may be cut from a 3 m length of timber? What length will remain?

PAPER 20

1. Simplify $2\frac{1}{2} - 1\frac{7}{8} + \frac{3}{4}$.

2. Calculate (a) $(36-24) \div (-8)$, (b) $36 - 24 \div 8$.

3. Write down the next two numbers in the sequence 5, 6, 8, 11, ...

4. Find the sum of all the numbers between 20 and 50 which are multiples of 8.

5. Two men walk at the same rate beginning with the same foot at the same time. If the first takes a pace of 75 cm and the second a pace of 80 cm, how far will they walk before they are in step again?

PAPER 21

1. Calculate (a) $9 - 3(6-4)$, (b) $(9-3)(6-4)$.

2. Express (a) $\frac{5}{16}$, (b) $\frac{4}{125}$ in decimals.

3. Divide 3.2 kg of potatoes between Susan and Christine so that Christine has 70 g more than Susan.

4. Find the HCF of 620, 1116 and 1488.

5. A clock loses 5 seconds every hour. If it is correct at 8 a.m. on Monday morning, how much will it have lost by the following Monday at the same time?

PAPER 22

1. Simplify $1\frac{2}{3} + 5\frac{1}{12} - 4\frac{3}{4}$.

2. Express (a) 0.875, (b) 0.218 75, as common fractions in their lowest terms.

3. Calculate (a) $6.4 \times 1.6 \times 2.4$, (b) $9.01 \div 1.7$.

4. How many packets, each containing 450 g, may be filled from a crate containing three-quarters of a tonne of mixed fruit? How much remains?

5. What is the smallest number of records that can be divided between 20, 24 or 30 girls?

PAPER 23

1. Simplify $\dfrac{4}{3}\left(1\dfrac{1}{4}-\dfrac{1}{5}\right)$.

2. Calculate $\dfrac{2^3 \times 3 \times 5^2}{2 \times 5^3}$.

3. (a) Find $217 - 0.217$. (b) Divide 0.2484 by 0.9.

4. Reduce 468 kg to a common fraction of 1 t in its lowest terms.

5. A journey by car which lasted 6 hours 37 minutes ended at 1 p.m. What time did it start?

PAPER 24

1. Express 960.747 correct to (a) the nearest hundred, (b) three significant figures, (c) one decimal place.

2. Which is the greater and by how much, $2\dfrac{1}{2}\times\dfrac{2}{3}$ or $2\dfrac{1}{2}\div\dfrac{2}{3}$?

3. Express 120 cm as a fraction of 8 m in its lowest terms.

4. Find the number which is half-way between -4 and 8.

5. If I give 0.375 of my ball of string to my sister, then half of what remains to my brother, I still have 4.3 m. How much string did I have to start with?

PAPER 25

1. Simplify $2\dfrac{13}{95}\div 2\dfrac{2}{57}$.

2. Find (a) 4.8×0.4, (b) $4.8\div0.04$, (c) $0.48\div40$.

3. Express 0.925 54 correct to (a) the nearest whole number, (b) two decimal places, (c) three significant figures.

4. State what part 85 cm is of 4 m as (a) a common fraction in its lowest terms, (b) a decimal fraction.

5. A water tank is $\frac{7}{8}$ full. If 5 litres is drawn off the tank is $\frac{13}{16}$ full. What quantity will the tank hold when full?

7

NUMBER SYSTEMS INCLUDING BINARY

EXAMPLE 1

$$37$$
$$26 +$$
$$\overline{65}$$

EXAMPLE 2

$$16$$
$$14$$
$$12 +$$
$$\overline{44}$$

At first sight the above examples seem very strange additions. Using the system we are most familiar with (the *denary* system) we would write:

$$37 \qquad\qquad 16$$
$$\underline{26} \quad \text{and} \quad 14$$
$$\overline{63} \qquad\qquad \underline{12}$$
$$\qquad\qquad\quad \overline{42}$$

These additions have been made in the scale of ten, i.e. we have used the rule: as soon as your total is 10, it is equal to one unit belonging to the next column to the left.

But if in Example 1 we give further information, and say that the first number refers to gallons while the second refers to pints, we can understand the addition that has taken place. The first line could be the amount of milk delivered to a canteen on Monday, while the second line could show the amount delivered on Tuesday. It follows that by adding the two together we have 6 gallons 5 pints, which is the amount delivered during the two days. Since 8 pints is equal to 1 gallon, the addition is correct. Here we have counted in base 8, or *octal* numbers.

Similarly, the second example shows the distances of three races in which the thoroughbred *Demur* ran. The distances are given in miles and furlongs, 8 furlongs being equivalent to 1 mile. Again we have counted in octal numbers.

These examples have only shown a single addition from one column to another, but they may be extended into the 'four rules' involving any base.

When we write 14_8 we refer to it as a number 'to the base 8'. The 1 to the left of the 4 is equal to 8 units. Thus $14_8 = (1 \times 8) + 4 = 8 + 4 = 12$ in our most commonly used system i.e. to the base 10 or in denary form.

Similarly
$$235_8 = (2 \times 8^2) + (3 \times 8) + 5$$
$$= 128 + 24 + 5$$
$$= 157_{10}$$

If we consider a base 5 number:
$$231_5 = (2 \times 5^2) + (3 \times 5) + 1$$
$$= 50 + 15 + 1$$
$$= 66_{10}$$

or a base 3 number:
$$121_3 = (1 \times 3^2) + (2 \times 3) + 1$$
$$= 9 + 6 + 1$$
$$= 16_{10}$$

Conversely, we may wish to convert a denary number into a number with a different base.

Thus
$$374 \text{ or } 374_{10} = (5 \times 64) + (6 \times 8) + 6$$

(arranging 374 as the sum of multiples of powers of 8)

i.e.
$$374_{10} = (5 \times 8^2) + (6 \times 8) + 6$$
$$= 566_8$$

The same result may also be obtained by dividing and writing remainders:

```
8 | 374 |
  8 | 46 | Rem 6
    8 | 5 | Rem 6
      0 | Rem 5
```

Writing the remainders from the bottom up gives:

$$374_{10} = 566_8$$

EXAMPLE 3   Convert the denary number 287 into a number to the base 5.

$$5\underline{|287|}$$
$$5\underline{|57|}\ \text{Rem 2}$$
$$5\underline{|11|}\ \text{Rem 2}$$
$$5\underline{|2|}\ \text{Rem 1}$$
$$0|\ \text{Rem 2}$$

$$\therefore\quad 287_{10}\ =\ 2122_5$$

The following examples show how the 'four rules' operate for different bases.

EXAMPLE 4   Find:

(a) $134_5 + 23_5$,

(b) $124_5 - 31_5$,

(c) $232_5 \times 12_5$,

(d) $121_5 \div 14_5$.

(a)	134	(b)	124	(c)	232	(d)	4
	23		31		12		14)121
	212		43		1014		121
					2320		. . .
					3334		

EXAMPLE 5   Find:

(a) $574_8 + 261_8$,

(b) $1543_8 - 725_8$,

(c) $342_8 \times 35_8$,

(d) $3410_8 \div 31_8$.

(a)	574	(b)	1543	(c)	342	(d)	110
	261		725		35		31)3410
	1055		616		2152		31
					10 460		31
					12 632		31
							0
							0

EXERCISE 33

Find:

1. $235_8 + 6$ 2. $542_8 + 5$ 3. $424_5 + 4$ 4. $134_5 + 3$

5. $212_3 + 2$ 6. $532_7 + 5$ 7. $342_8 - 7$ 8. $572_8 - 5$

9. $421_5 - 4$ 10. $341_5 - 3$ 11. $352_6 - 5$.

12. Convert the following octal numbers into denary numbers: 23_8, 542_8, 267_8, 534_8.

13. Convert the following base 3 numbers into denary numbers: 22_3, 212_3, 1212_3, 2111_3.

14. Convert the following base 4 four numbers into denary numbers: 32_4, 123_4, 322_4, 1232_4.

15. Convert the denary numbers 34, 267 and 534 into (a) numbers to the base 5, (b) numbers to the base 7.

16. Find (a) $424_5 + 133_5$, (b) $213_5 - 34_5$.

17. Find (a) $374_8 + 166_8$, (b) $525_8 - 266_8$.

18. Find (a) $327_8 \times 121_8$, (b) $6335_8 \div 45_8$.

19. Find (a) $341_5 \times 223_5$, (b) $200222_3 \div 121_3$.

20. Calculate (a) $346_7 + 214_7 + 523_7$, (b) $331_4 + 123_4 - 231_4$.

Find each of the following, working in the given base:

21. (a) $212_3 + 112_3$, (b) $214_6 \times 23_6$, (c) $1220_6 \div 41_6$.

22. (a) $2345_9 - 1264_9$, (b) $225_7 \times 46_7$, (c) $2134_5 \div 3_5$.

23. (a) $4341_5 + 3122_5$, (b) $7533_8 - 3452_8$, (c) $221_3 \times 111_3$.

24. (a) $6453_7 - 655_7$, (b) $332_4 \times 213_4$, (c) $5027_8 \div 173_8$.

25. (a) $677_8 \div 245_8$, (b) $4332_5 \div 2113_5$.

BINARY NUMBERS

The smallest base we can use is 2. The only two symbols then required are 0 and 1. This system is called the *binary* system. It is extremely important in computer work because the electronic circuits can only be in one of two states — *on* or *off*. A binary number is built up of powers of 2.

i.e. $\qquad 10101_2 = (1 \times 2^4) + (0 \times 2^3) + (1 \times 2^2) + (0 \times 2^1) + (1 \times 2^0)$

NOTE: $a^0 = 1$ for any non-zero value of a. In particular, $2^0 = 1$ or $1 = 2^0$.

$$= 16 + 0 + 4 + 0 + 1$$

$$= 21_{10}$$

and $\qquad 1110111_2 = (1 \times 2^6) + (1 \times 2^5) + (1 \times 2^4) + (0 \times 2^3)$
$$+ (1 \times 2^2) + (1 \times 2^1) + (1 \times 2^0)$$

$$= 64 + 32 + 16 + 0 + 4 + 2 + 1$$

$$= 119_{10}$$

EXAMPLE 6

Convert 78_{10} into a binary number.

Method 1 $78 = 64 + 8 + 4 + 2$

$$= 2^6 + 2^3 + 2^2 + 2^1$$

If we now introduce zeros for the powers of 2 which are missing, $78 = 2^6 + 0 + 0 + 2^3 + 2^2 + 2^1 + 0$

$\therefore$ $78_{10} = 1001110_2$

Method 2   Using division by 2 and remainders we have:

```
2 |78|
2 |39| Rem 0
2 |19| Rem 1
 2 |9| Rem 1
 2 |4| Rem 1
 2 |2| Rem 0
 2 |1| Rem 0
  0| Rem 1
```

i.e. the binary equivalent, writing from the bottom up, is 1001110_2.

EXAMPLE 7

Convert the binary number 111001111_2 to denary.

$$111001111_2 = 2^7 + 2^6 + 2^5 + 2^2 + 2^1 + 2^0$$

$$= 128 + 64 + 32 + 4 + 2 + 1$$

$$= 231_{10}$$

EXERCISE 34

Convert the following denary numbers into binary:

1. 9	2. 11	3. 17	4. 19
5. 24	6. 27	7. 36	8. 45
9. 57	10. 69	11. 96	12. 105
13. 126	14. 137	15. 153	16. 172
17. 193	18. 218	19. 253	20. 342.

Convert the following binary numbers into denary:

21. 110	22. 111	23. 1001	24. 1100
25. 1011	26. 1101	27. 10110	28. 11001
29. 10111	30. 10011	31. 11111	
32. 101010	33. 110011	34. 101110	
35. 100111	36. 111001.		

37. What is the largest denary number which can be represented by five binary digits?

38. What is the largest denary number which can be represented by seven binary digits?

Which is the larger of the following pairs of binary numbers?

39. 110, 101

40. 1011, 1100

41. 10101, 1111

42. 110101, 111000.

Which is the smaller of the following pairs of binary numbers?

43. 1011, 1100

44. 10111, 10101

45. 11000, 11001

46. 101011, 101100.

47. Which of the following binary numbers are even?
    (a) 100   (b) 1000   (c) 1101   (d) 11001
    (e) 11000.

48. Which of the following binary numbers are odd?
    (a) 1001   (b) 1100   (c) 10001   (d) 11111
    (e) 10000.

49. Which of the following binary numbers are multiples of 4?
    (a) 101   (b) 100   (c) 100100
    (d) 1100110   (e) 111110.

50. Which of the following binary numbers are multiples of 8?
    (a) 1010   (b) 10110   (c) 11000   (d) 101100
    (e) 10001.

51. Write down:
    (a) the next three binary numbers after 1101110
    (b) the next three odd numbers after 1101011
    (c) the next two even numbers after 101101.

52. Write down the binary number which is 4 more than 101111.

53. Write down the binary number which is 6 more than 10111.

54. Write down the binary number which is 2 less than 110110.

55. Write down the binary number which is 5 less than 110011.

BINARY ADDITION

Facts worth learning are:

$$1 + 1 = 10$$

$$1 + 1 + 1 = 11$$

and $$1 + 1 + 1 + 1 = 100$$

EXAMPLE 8

```
   1011
    111
  10010
    111
```

In the right hand column $1+1=10$ i.e. 0 down carry 1. In the second column we have $1+1+1$ (carried) $=11$ i.e. 1 down carry 1, and so on. When your total is 2 in any column it is 'worth' 1 in the next column to the left.

EXAMPLE 9

```
   1110
    101
  11101
   1011
 111011
   1111
     11
```

BINARY SUBTRACTION

EXAMPLE 10

(a)
```
 1101
  111 −
  110
```

(b)
```
 10011
  1110 −
   101
```

When you use 1 from the previous column it is worth 2 in the column in which it is used.

BINARY MULTIPLICATION

EXAMPLE 11

(a)
```
    111
     11×
    111
   1110
  10101
```

(b)
```
    1101
     110×
   11010
  110100
 1001110
```

BINARY DIVISION

With binary division, instead of thinking 'How many times?', think 'Will it divide?'. If the answer is 'Yes', a 1 goes in the answer, but if the answer is 'No', then a 0 goes in the answer.

EXAMPLE 12

(a) Divide 10101 by 111.

(b) Divide 11011 by 101.

(c) Divide 10011101 by 1011.

(a)
```
          11
   111)10101
        111
        111
        111
        . . .
```

(b)
$$101\overline{)11011}\quad\quad\frac{101}{}$$

i.e. 1 0 1 remainder 10

```
         101
101)11011
     101
     111
     101
      10
```

(c)
i.e. 1 1 1 0 remainder
11

```
          1110
1011)10011101
      1011
      10001
       1011
       1100
       1011
         11
```

EXERCISE 35

Working in the binary system, add:

1. 1 0 1 0
    1 1
    ———

2. 1 1 0 1
    1 0 1
    ———

3. 1 0 1 0
    1 1 1
    ———

4. 1 1 1
    1 1 1
    ——

5. 1 0 1 1
    1 1 0 0
    ———

6. 1 1 0 0 1
    1 1 1 1
    ———

7. 1 1 0 1 1
    1 0 1 1
    ———

8. 1 0 1 1 1 0
    1 1 1 0 1
    ———

9. 1 0 1
    1 1 1
    1 0 0 1
    ———

10. 1 1 1
     1 1
     1 1 0 0
     ———

11. 1 0 1 1
     1 1 1
     1 1 0 0
     ———

12. 1 1 0 0 1
     1 1 0 0
     1 1 1
     ———

13. 1 1 0 0 1 1
     1 1 1 1
     1 0 1 0 1
     1 0 1
     ———

14. 1 0 0 0 1 1
     1 0 0 1 1
     1 1 1 1
     1 0 0 0 1
     ———

Working in the binary system, perform the following subtractions:

15. 1 1 0
     1 1
     ——

16. 1 0 0 1
     1 1 1
     ———

17. 1 1 0 0
     1 1 1
     ———

18. 1 1 0 1
     1 1
     ———

19. 1 1 1 0 0
     1 0 1
     ———

20. 1 0 1 0 1
     1 1 1
     ———

21. 1 1 0 0 1 1
     1 1 1 0
     ———

22. 1 0 1 1 0 1
     1 0 1 1 0
     ———

Working in the binary system, perform the following multiplications:

23. 110×11

24. 1011×11

25. 1100×11

26. 1010×110

27. 1100×101

28. 1010×111

29. 1100×1010

30. 1011×1011

31. 101010×110.

Working in the binary system, divide:

32. 1010 by 10

33. 11011 by 11

34. 111000 by 1110

35. 10011010 by 1011

36. 10010110 by 1010

37. 1101 by 110

38. 101110 by 111

39. 110110 by 101

40. 100011 by 110.

8

MONEY

THE UK SYSTEM

In the United Kingdom the basic unit of currency is the pound sterling (£) which is divided into 100 pence (p)

i.e. £1 = 100 p

A decimal point is used to separate the pounds from the pence, hence £7.43 means seven pounds and forty-three pence. When the £ sign has been used it is unnecessary to write the pence sign after the pence.

There are two ways of writing amounts less than one pound. Forty-three pence may be written either £0.43 or 43 p. If the number of pence is less than ten, we place a zero in front of the number if we use the £ sign; e.g. three pence may be written 3 p or £0.03.

The smallest unit of money used is the half-penny, which is written as a common fraction i.e. $\frac{1}{2}$. Three and a half pence is thus written $3\frac{1}{2}$ p or £0.03$\frac{1}{2}$. It is worth noting that this is equivalent to £0.035, a fact which is useful in some questions.

ADDITION

EXERCISE 36

Add:

1. £	2. £	3. £	4. £
0.42	0.24	0.15	0.11
0.16	0.35	0.42	0.22
0.21	0.40	0.31	0.55

5. £
0.14
0.47
0.34
———

6. £
0.22
0.39
0.17
———

7. £
0.35
0.26
0.37
———

8. £
0.54
0.12
0.29
———

9. £
0.44
0.37
0.92
———

10. £
0.53
0.74
0.66
———

11. £
0.73
0.94
0.36
———

12. £
0.84
0.78
0.59
———

13. £
1.26
5.93
7.21
———

14. £
4.62
3.93
8.21
———

15. £
5.66
14.29
3.24
———

16. £
21.43
9.26
8.73
———

17. £
8.17
2.04
8.36
———

18. £
12.24
23.61
14.40
———

19. £
8.30
4.75
2.99
———

20. £
3.17
4.92
7.36
———

21. £
$0.37\frac{1}{2}$
$0.42\frac{1}{2}$
$0.83\frac{1}{2}$
———

22. £
$0.15\frac{1}{2}$
$0.74\frac{1}{2}$
$0.30\frac{1}{2}$
———

23. £
$0.29\frac{1}{2}$
$0.13\frac{1}{2}$
$0.48\frac{1}{2}$
———

24. £
$0.16\frac{1}{2}$
$0.42\frac{1}{2}$
$0.78\frac{1}{2}$
———

25. £
$4.09\frac{1}{2}$
$6.33\frac{1}{2}$
$4.58\frac{1}{2}$
———

26. £
$3.72\frac{1}{2}$
1.36
$4.97\frac{1}{2}$
———

27. £
$6.90\frac{1}{2}$
$5.46\frac{1}{2}$
1.32
———

28. £
4.68
$9.39\frac{1}{2}$
$8.21\frac{1}{2}$
———

29. £
14.34
$8.92\frac{1}{2}$
76.40
4.62
———

30. £
42.40
$17.26\frac{1}{2}$
8.37
50.21
———

31. £
127.41
4.93
18.21
227.03
———

32. £
5.92
36.14
127.03
9.78
———

33.	£	34.	£	35.	£	36.	£
	14.90		30.21		4.36		$8.14\frac{1}{2}$
	7.36		520.72		413.74		33.54
	532.40		18.43		8.93		$4.92\frac{1}{2}$
	0.67		227.16		55.29		127.30

37.	£	38.	£	39.	£	40.	£
	226.41		154.14		$246.44\frac{1}{2}$		$726.43\frac{1}{2}$
	128.49		726.80		893.53		436.13
	307.52		819.56		$254.62\frac{1}{2}$		$293.59\frac{1}{2}$
	78.90		334.72		726.18		$874.73\frac{1}{2}$

41. $£8.23\frac{1}{2} + £37.40 + £14.04$

42. $£48.26\frac{1}{2} + £59.13 + £88.47$

43. $£73.74 + £16.92 + £57.26\frac{1}{2}$

44. $£80.21 + £18.28\frac{1}{2} + £66.90\frac{1}{2}$

45. $£246.40 + £82 + £2.76 + £34.42$

46. $£52.42 + £218.74 + 99\,p + £7.62$

47. $£8.32\frac{1}{2} + £346.74 + £72.58\frac{1}{2} + £19.87\frac{1}{2}$

48. $£17.62\frac{1}{2} + £843.42 + £78.13\frac{1}{2} + £227.13\frac{1}{2}$

49. $£26.42\frac{1}{2} + 44\frac{1}{2}\,p + 16\,p + £5.14$

50. The table below shows the daily takings (in £) in a shop over a four week period:

	M	T	W	T	F	S	
WEEK 1	20.16	54.91	70.14	737.93	1036.14	942.10	g
WEEK 2	50.92	16.31	53.56	623.87	873.59	837.31	h
WEEK 3	78.44	34.80	49.08	672.74	1137.44	742.78	i
WEEK 4	18.44	93.72	61.82	852.68	936.95	529.37	j
	a	b	c	d	e	f	k

Add the columns and rows. Find the total by adding the answers for the rows and check your answer by totalling the answers to the columns.

SUBTRACTION

EXERCISE 37

Subtract:

1. £
   7.36
   4.14
   ___

2. £
   9.35
   6.31
   ___

3. £
   3.94
   1.82
   ___

4. £
   6.67
   4.36
   ___

5. £
   9.27
   4.63
   ___

6. £
   6.14
   1.82
   ___

7. £
   4.47
   2.98
   ___

8. £
   8.13
   5.95
   ___

9. £
   $4.27\frac{1}{2}$
   1.82
   ___

10. £
    $7.42\frac{1}{2}$
    3.58
    ___

11. £
    $8.59\frac{1}{2}$
    5.62
    ___

12. £
    $13.29\frac{1}{2}$
    7.36
    ___

13. £
    24.16
    $18.09\frac{1}{2}$
    ___

14. £
    52.43
    $9.27\frac{1}{2}$
    ___

15. £
    38.19
    $9.36\frac{1}{2}$
    ___

16. £
    82.76
    $34.83\frac{1}{2}$
    ___

17. £
    50.00
    9.38
    ___

18. £
    170.00
    54.16
    ___

19. £
    280.00
    137.94
    ___

20. £
    200.00
    184.14
    ___

21. £
    529.00
    $136.87\frac{1}{2}$
    ___

22. £
    706.44
    $519.27\frac{1}{2}$
    ___

23. £
    400.49
    $126.84\frac{1}{2}$
    ___

24. £
    563.92
    $398.77\frac{1}{2}$
    ___

25. £
    2000.00
    816.94
    ___

26. £
    5000.00
    4937.61
    ___

27. £
    4396.14
    $2847.38\frac{1}{2}$
    ___

28. £
    $9264.08\frac{1}{2}$
    5648.29
    ___

29. £50 − £28.34

30. £82 − £69.87

31. £180 − £93.51

32. £260.40 − £127.84

33. £349.21 − £253.97

34. £545.06 − £387.93

35. £413.40 − £278.65

36. £47.04 − £$38.58\frac{1}{2}$

37. £134.92 − £82.76½

38. £9.82½ − £3.76½

39. £349.20½ − £261.08½

40. £1600.12½ − £834.37½.

Subtract the first amount from the second:

41. 87 p, £4.22

42. 15½ p, £8.00

43. £2.44, £12.16

44. £76.84½, £100

45. £382.79½, £579.06.

Subtract the second amount from the first:

46. £10, £8.16

47. £40, £26.49½

48. £57.44, £42.83½

49. £826.93, £536.28

50. £714.47, £73.84½.

MULTIPLICATION

EXERCISE 38

Multiply:

1. £2.44 by 3

2. £6.13 by 4

3. £4.73 by 5

4. £1.63 by 6

5. £5.19 by 7

6. £8.59 by 8

7. £3.74 by 10

8. £9.73 by 9

9. £4.32 by 11

10. £6.64 by 7

11. £8.84 by 8

12. £3.68 by 5

13. £4.87 by 4

14. £9.26 by 6

15. £1.37 by 8

16. £5.82½ by 6

17. £7.51½ by 8

18. £3.18½ by 10

19. £6.74½ by 3

20. £4.42½ by 5

21. £8.27½ by 9

22. £5.92 by 14

23. £6.59 by 16

24. £9.32 by 18

25. £1.47 by 15

26. £3.92 by 17

27. £8.62 by 19

28. £6.73$\frac{1}{2}$ by 12

29. £7.16$\frac{1}{2}$ by 15

30. £4.29$\frac{1}{2}$ by 18

31. £24.16 by 26

32. £73.34 by 33

33. £49.37 by 54

34. £16.49 by 37

35. £92.03 by 57

36. £70.64 by 83

37. £36.24$\frac{1}{2}$ by 46

38. £19.87$\frac{1}{2}$ by 54

39. £23.64$\frac{1}{2}$ by 82

40. £84.73$\frac{1}{2}$ by 53

41. £39.27$\frac{1}{2}$ by 77

42. £60.58$\frac{1}{2}$ by 39

43. £136.40 by 46

44. £234.56 by 36

45. £343.82 by 86

46. £413.90 by 73

47. £291.50 by 95

48. £186.43 by 47

49. £182.61$\frac{1}{2}$ by 34

50. £763.90 by 47.

DIVISION

EXERCISE 39

Divide:

1. £4.89 by 3

2. £11.35 by 5

3. £7.98 by 7

4. £16.64 by 8

5. £12.15 by 9

6. £23.76 by 11

7. £43.36 by 8

8. £39.24 by 9

9. £32.76 by 12

10. £93.08 by 13

11. £74.34 by 18

12. £39.69 by 21

13. £149.58 by 27

14. £134.64 by 17

15. £223.72 by 34

16. £156.94 by 38

17. £231.50 by 25

18. £71.82 by 19

19. £69.66 by 43

20. £151.28 by 62

21. £290.08 by 56

22. £133.28 by 28

23. £245.29 by 19

24. £421.82 by 23

25. £449.28 by 72

26. £589.38 by 66

27. £374.36 by 49	28. £399.36 by 39
29. £75.44 by 46	30. £511.56 by 28
31. £511.98 by 53	32. £351.96 by 42
33. £795.63 by 33	34. £23.76 by 54 p
35. £27.36 by 72 p	36. £39.56 by 43 p
37. £48 by 75 p	38. £22.62 by 29 p
39. £48.14 by 83 p	40. £51.12 by £1.42
41. £168.54 by £3.18	42. £214.08 by £4.46
43. £192.78 by £1.89	44. £962.88 by £4.72
45. £783.96 by £8.34	46. £54.90 by 36
47. £204.39 by 54	48. £585.23 by 86
49. £1190.99½ by 73	50. £143.37½ by 31
51. £465.40½ by 57	52. £239.94 by 124
53. £555.45 by 230	54. £1351.35 by 182
55. £5.51 by 14½ p	56. £15.67½ by 27½ p
57. £46.35½ by 63½ p	58. £1435.50 by £12.37½
59. £5516.08 by £18.14½	60. £7686.22½ by £39.82½.

EXERCISE 40 MISCELLANEOUS EXAMPLES

1. A father changes a £5 note and gives £1.27 to each of his three children. How much is left over?

2. How many complete metres of cloth at £3.80 a metre may be bought for £20? What sum of money is left over?

3. Calculate the cost of 760 units of electricity at 4.55 p per unit.

4. Calculate the cost of 376 therms of gas at 32.5 p per therm.

5. During a day's work a bus driver collected 184 fares at 72 p each, 147 at 54 p each and 34 at 44 p each. How much did he collect during the day?

6. The total tickets sold for a concert were as follows: 154 at £6, 243 at £4 and 193 at £3. Find the total amount of money collected.

7. If a 2 p piece is 2.6 cm in diameter, find the value of 1 km of 2 p pieces laid side by side.

8. Jane Goldspink went shopping with the knowledge that she had £216.40 in her bank account. She wrote cheques to the value of

£41.67, £16.93, £53.19 and £39.47. How much remained in her account after these cheques had been passed?

9. A book of postage stamps contains 12 stamps at $22\frac{1}{2}$ p each, 6 stamps at 18 p each and 6 stamps at $16\frac{1}{2}$ p each. Find the total value of the book.

10. A family of five bought their Christmas cards. Father bought 42 at 16 p each, mother 45 at 18 p each, John 16 at 10 p each, Joan 18 at 9 p each and Jack 26 at 8 p each. How many cards did they buy? How much did they spend on cards altogether? How much would it cost to send all these cards if the postage for each was 18 p?

11. In a school canteen 85 pupils bought the 65 p meal, 64 the 58 p meal and 116 the meal costing 52 p. Find the total takings.

12. A school decided that they could afford to give £360 away in book tokens for Prize Day. If they gave tokens to the value of £5 but each token cost an extra 5 p, find the maximum number of prizes they could afford.

13. How many 50 g balls of wool could be purchased for £20 if each ball cost 76 p? How much cash was left over?

14. Bread rolls for refreshments at a disco cost 15 p each. How many rolls could be purchased for £12?

15. When milk costs 25 p per pint a family take 4 pints every day except Tuesday and Thursday when they take 3. Calculate the weekly milk bill.

16. Find the cost of buying 748 roofing tiles at 96 p each.

17. Four tyres for a car cost £45.13 each. What change would there be from £200?

18. A generous teacher gave Christmas presents to his class. He gave $\frac{1}{2}$ p to the first pupil, 1 p to the second, 2 p to the third, 4 p to the fourth, 8 p to the fifth, and so on. If there were 12 children in the class, how much did it cost him?

19. In one week in a school tuck shop they sold 162 bars of chocolate at 44 p each, 247 cans of squash at 35 p each and 942 packets of crisps at 15 p each. Find the total takings for the week.

20. The Hussett's daily newspaper costs 32 p, the Sunday paper 45 p, and in addition they take magazines each week to the value of £1.54. How much change will there be if they pay for the week's papers with a £5 note?

21. A money box contains £14 in 5 p, 10 p and 50 p coins. If there are twenty-three 50 p coins and eighteen 10 p coins, how many 5 p coins are there?

22. A collecting box contains £9.41 in coins of value 2 p, 5 p and 10 p. If there are twenty-seven 5 p coins and seventy 10 p coins, how many 2 p coins are there?

23. When the collecting box for the blind on the counter of the local shop is opened it is found to contain the following coins: 48 at 1 p, 55 at 2 p, 37 at 10 p and five at 50 p. How much was in the box?

24. Sandra takes part in a sponsored 8 mile walk. Thirteen people sponsor her for 2 p a mile, twenty-one for 5 p a mile and eight people for 50 p a mile. How much should she collect if she walks the whole distance?

25. Find the cost of 4.5 t at £133.60 per tonne.

26. Anthony Thompson's 'take-home' pay is £98.70 per week for a five day week. If it costs him 84 p per day in bus fares, £1.44 per day for lunch, and he pays £22.50 each week towards his keep, how much remains?

27. A builder sells a new house for £38 000. If the materials cost him £14 550 and he employed eight men for 52 days at £48 each per day, how much profit did he make?

28. A school decides to spend £6000 on re-equipping the school library. An Open Day in aid of this raises £2543.80, and 563 parents each promise to donate £2.50. How much is still required?

29. Seven hundred and thirty-two factory workers negotiate a pay increase of 6 p per hour for a thirty-eight hour week. How much will this cost the company?

30. Forty-seven office workers negotiate an 8 p per hour increase for a thirty-seven hour week. Find the increase in the firm's weekly wage bill.

31. A group of forty-two fourth formers pay £142 each to go on a short holiday to France. In addition they each pay in £45 for pocket money. Calculate the total amount of money collected.

32. A man's 'take-home' pay, after all deductions, is £94.50 per week. How much is his 'take-home' pay for the year?

33. The school under-12 soccer team, plus a teacher and one reserve, go to an away game by bus. If the teacher's return fare is £2.42, but all the boys travel for half fare, find the total paid in fares.

34. A woman's annual salary is £10 400. If she pays £832 pension contribution and £191 per calendar month in income tax, calculate her net annual salary.

35. A dining table costs £345.50, a dining chair £85.40 and a carver (a dining chair with arms) £112.37. What would be the total cost of a table and eight chairs, two of which are carvers?

36. A gardener is paid £2.54 per hour, and his helper £1.86 per hour. How much would they earn between them in a four week month if each works for 38 hours a week?

37. The return fare to London, which is 144 miles away, is £21.60. How much is this per mile?

38. The single fare to Manchester, which is 276 km away is £17.94. What is the charge per kilometre?

39. If there are 158 people employed in a department store and each employee earns on average £94 per week, calculate the weekly wage bill.

40. A company agrees to the weekly wages of its 764 employees being increased from £144 to £156.50 if fifty-five employees retire early. Does the weekly wage bill increase or decrease, and by how much?

41. Ernie Tamplin buys a second hand car for £760, spends £25 each on four new tyres, and spends a further £158 on repairs. Later he sells it for £1050. Find his profit (or loss).

42. Mr Cooper pays for his car by making a down payment of £520 followed by 24 monthly payments of £84.36. How much does his car cost him?

43. In the January sales a man buys three shirts at £7.50 each (reduced from £14.50), two ties at £1.75 each (reduced from £2.25) and six pairs of socks at 80 p per pair (reduced from £1.20). How much did he save by waiting for the sale?

44. A housewife makes 14 kg of marmalade using 4 kg of oranges at 60 p per kg, 8 kg of sugar at 44 p per kg and 10 lemons at 15 p each. Find the cost per kilogram of the marmalade.

45. Mrs Miles changes £156 into French francs, and for each £ she receives 9 francs. How many francs does she receive?

46. Mr Woodward changes 968 US dollars into sterling. If he receives 55 p for each dollar, how many £s does he receive?

47. A cashier in a bank has a bundle of £10 notes which are numbered consecutively from S52 001013 to S52 001246. What is the value of the bundle?

48. John Shepherd buys a motorcycle by paying a deposit of £72 followed by thirty-six monthly payments of £14.56. Paying on terms costs him £22.66 more than the cash price. Calculate the cash price.

49. 357 000 people enter for a 'Win-a-car' competition in a newspaper. If the entry fee is 25 p, and the prizes are five cars, each car being valued at £8450, find the profit made by the newspaper.

50. An ironmonger mixes 12 kg of nails costing £3.60 per kilogram with 36 kg of nails costing £4.20 per kilogram. What is the cost per kilogram of the mixture?

9

AVERAGES

If a batsman scores 56, 49, 81 and 34 in four completed innings we say that his average score is $\dfrac{56 + 49 + 81 + 34}{4} = 55$. While he has not scored exactly 55 in any particular innings, the figure enables us to compare him with another batsman who has scored 520 in 10 completed innings and has an average of 52.

Similarly, if a train travels 150 miles in $1\frac{1}{2}$ hours, we say that the average speed of the train is $\dfrac{150}{1\frac{1}{2}}$ mph $= 100$ mph.

The *average* (or *mean*) of a number of quantities is the total of all the quantities divided by the number of quantities.

i.e. the average of $N_1, N_2, N_3, \ldots, N_m$

$$= \frac{N_1 + N_2 + N_3 + \ldots + N_m}{m}$$

It is particularly important to remember that you cannot add or subtract averages. Always deal in totals.

EXAMPLE 1   The Saturday takings of a small shop over a four week period are £212, £164, £178 and £174. Find the average Saturday takings over the four weeks.

Average takings $= £\dfrac{212 + 164 + 178 + 174}{4}$

$= £\dfrac{728}{4}$

$= £182$

EXAMPLE 2

In a rugby team the average weight of the seven backs is 76 kg and the average weight of the eight forwards is 90 kg. Find the average weight of the team, giving your answer correct to one decimal place.

Total weight of the seven backs $= 7 \times 76$ kg
$$= 532 \text{ kg}$$
Total weight of the eight forwards $= 8 \times 90$ kg
$$= 720 \text{ kg}$$
Total weight of the fifteen team members $= 1252$ kg

$\therefore$ Average weight of team $= \dfrac{1252}{15}$ kg $= 83.47$ kg

$$= 83.5 \text{ kg correct to one decimal place}$$

EXAMPLE 3

A girl sets out on a 7 mile journey on her bicycle. She rides for 5 miles at an average speed of 15 mph until her bicycle breaks down, forcing her to push the bicycle the remaining distance at a speed of 3 mph. Find her average speed for the whole journey.

Time spent riding $= \dfrac{5 \text{ miles}}{15 \text{ mph}} = \dfrac{1}{3}$ hour

Time spent pushing $= \dfrac{2}{3}$ hour

$\therefore$ Total time for journey $= \left(\dfrac{1}{3} + \dfrac{2}{3} \right)$ hours

$$= 1 \text{ hour}$$

Average speed for whole journey $= \dfrac{\text{total distance}}{\text{total time}}$

$$= \dfrac{10 \text{ miles}}{1 \text{ hour}}$$

$$= 10 \text{ mph}$$

EXERCISE 41

Find the average of:

1. 10, 12, 14, 16, 18
2. 56, 48, 60, 57, 49
3. 57, 34, 42, 29, 38
4. 8.2, 12.4, 16.5, 9.9, 11.2, 17.4
5. 27.2, 34.9, 46.7, 39.4, 53.1, 39.9.

6. The number of hours of sunshine in Corfu for successive days during a certain week were 10.4, 12.6, 11.4, 8.2, 12.2, 12.4, 9.8. Find the daily average.

7. A car takes $2\frac{1}{4}$ hours for a journey of $128\frac{1}{4}$ miles. Calculate its average speed.

8. A coach takes $3\frac{1}{3}$ hours for a journey of 300 kilometres. Calculate its average speed.

9. Joan takes 8 minutes to walk the $\frac{1}{2}$ mile to school. Find her average walking speed in mph.

10. George cycles from school to his home, a distance of $4\frac{1}{2}$ miles, in 15 minutes. Find his average speed in mph.

11. Caroline takes 24 minutes to walk to her friend's home which is 2 km away. Find her average walking speed in kilometres per hour.

12. In an ice-dancing competition the marks awarded to a couple were: 5.4, 4.9, 5.8, 5.5, 5.7, 5.5, 5.5, 5.4. Their score is found by finding the average of these marks but ignoring the highest and lowest marks. Calculate the couple's score.

13. A county bowler takes 110 wickets for 1267 runs. Find his bowling average correct to two decimal places.

14. An opening batsman scores 1976 runs in a season in 46 completed innings. Calculate his average correct to two decimal places.

15. Last season a batsman scored 976 runs in 38 completed innings, while the season before he scored 1242 runs in 43 completed innings. Calculate his average over the two seasons, giving your answer correct to one decimal place.

16. In the first 20 innings of a season a batsman scored 1124 runs. In the next innings he scored 136. By how much will this increase his average?

17. The average number of newspapers sold by a newsagent from Monday to Friday during a certain week was 483, while the average number sold from Monday to Saturday of the same week was 516. How many papers were sold on the Saturday?

18. The average height of 25 girls in a form was 152.2 cm. When one girl joined the class the average fell to 152 cm. How tall was she?

19. My average petrol consumption for a 280 mile journey was 35 mpg. If the average consumption for 220 miles of the journey when I used the motorway was 40 mpg, calculate the number of miles per gallon for the 60 miles of urban driving.

20. A boy walks the $\frac{1}{4}$ mile from his home to the bus stop at an average speed of 3 mph. There he catches the bus which takes him the 10 miles to school at an average speed of 30 mph. Find his average speed for the whole journey.

21. A bus travels from Rainhill to Puddletown, a distance of 10 miles, at an average speed of 20 mph, and continues its journey to Wetside, a further 20 miles beyond Puddletown, at an average speed of 15 mph. Find its average speed for the whole journey from Rainhill to Wetside.

22. A motorist leaves home on a journey of 200 miles. The journey is in two distinct parts: the first 20 miles to the motorway is driven at an average speed of 20 mph, but once on the motorway he is able to average 60 mph. Calculate his average speed for the whole journey.

23. The area of the County of Eastshire is $50\,000\,km^2$ while the area of the County of Westshire is $20\,000\,km^2$. If the average annual rainfall for Eastshire is 254 cm while the average annual rainfall for Westshire is 317 cm, find the average annual rainfall for the two counties taken as a whole.

24. The average weight of the 12 boys in a class is 54.2 kg while the average weight of the 16 girls is 56.8 kg. Calculate the average weight for the whole class, giving your answer correct to one decimal place.

25. The average height of the 18 girls in a needlework class is 154 cm. If one girl leaves, the average height falls to 153.8 cm. How tall is she?

26. The area of the Republic of Ireland is approximately 27 000 square miles, while the area of Northern Ireland is approximately 5500 square miles. During a certain year the average rainfall in the Republic amounted to 920 mm, while the average rainfall in the North was 1040 mm. Calculate the average rainfall for Ireland. Give your answer correct to the nearest millimetre.

27. In a boat race the average mass of a crew is 67.8 kg. If the mass of the cox is 43 kg, find the average mass of the oarsmen.

28. A first division football club had an average 'home' gate of 21 400 for the first half of the season when they played 12 games, but an average 'home' gate of 23 700 for the 9 games played during the second half of the season. Find the average 'home' gate for the season, giving your answer correct to the nearest 100.

29. Peter's journey from home to London consisted of three distinct parts. He walked the $\frac{1}{2}$ mile from home to the bus stop at 4 mph, travelled the 10 miles by bus to the station at an average speed of 20 mph, and the 150 miles from the station to London at an average speed of 100 mph. Calculate his average speed from home to London.

30. A motorist wanted to make a 110 mile journey in 2 hours. He travelled the first 60 miles at an average speed of 45 mph, and the next 30 miles at an average speed of 90 mph. What must be his average speed for the final 20 miles if he is to arrive on time?

10 RATIO AND PROPORTION

If the length of the model of a railway carriage is 25 cm while the actual carriage is 18 m long, there is a relation between the two lengths. We say that the model is $\frac{1}{72}$ the length of the carriage. If the model is accurate, every linear dimension will be $\frac{1}{72}$ that of the actual carriage. We call this fraction the *ratio* between the lengths for the model and the corresponding lengths for the carriage. It is also convenient to write the ratio $\frac{1}{72}$ as $1:72$.

A ratio can exist only between two quantities of the same kind which have been expressed in the same units. It is always equivalent to a fraction which is an abstract number, and should be expressed as simply as possible.

If Joan has 20 p and Terry £1.35, the ratio

$$\frac{\text{Amount of money Joan has}}{\text{Amount of money Terry has}} = \frac{20\,\text{p}}{135\,\text{p}} = \frac{4}{27}$$

Conversely

$$\frac{\text{Amount of money Terry has}}{\text{Amount of money Joan has}} = \frac{27}{4}$$

A ratio is unaltered if the top and bottom are multiplied (or divided) by the same number.

e.g.

$$\frac{20}{135} = \frac{4}{27} = \frac{80}{540}$$

or

$$20:135 = 4:27 = 80:540$$

EXAMPLE 1

Find the ratio of 45 mm to 15 cm in its simplest form.

$$\text{Ratio} = \frac{45\,\text{mm}}{150\,\text{mm}}$$

$$= \frac{3}{10} \qquad \text{(dividing top and bottom by 15)}$$

EXAMPLE 2

Which ratio is the greater, $2:3$ or $5:8$?

$$\frac{2}{3} = \frac{16}{24} \quad \text{and} \quad \frac{5}{8} = \frac{15}{24}$$

$\therefore\ 2:3$ is the greater ratio.

EXAMPLE 3

Fill in the blanks in the following ratios:

$$\frac{5}{3} = \frac{15}{} = \frac{}{48}$$

$$\frac{5}{3} = \frac{15}{9} \qquad (15 = 5 \times 3 \ \therefore \text{ denominator is multiplied by 3 to give 9})$$

$$= \frac{80}{48} \qquad (48 = 3 \times 16 \ \therefore \text{ numerator is multiplied by 16 to give 80})$$

EXAMPLE 4

Increase £5 in the ratio $12:5$.

$$\text{Required amount} = £5 \times \frac{12}{5} = £12$$

EXAMPLE 5

Decrease 36 cm in the ratio $4:9$.

$$\text{Required length} = 36 \times \frac{4}{9} \text{ cm} = 16 \text{ cm}$$

EXAMPLE 6

When the cost of gas increases in the ratio $7:5$ a household cuts its use of gas in the ratio $3:4$. In what ratio will the total cost alter?

The increase in the cost of gas causes the bill to be multiplied by a factor of $\frac{7}{5}$.

The reduction in use causes the bill to be multiplied by a factor of $\frac{3}{4}$.

$\therefore$ The effect of the two changes is to multiply the bill by $\frac{7}{5} \times \frac{3}{4}$ or $\frac{21}{20}$, i.e. the bill will be increased in the ratio $21:20$.

EXERCISE 42

Express the following ratios as fractions in their lowest terms:

1. $20:30$ 2. $25:45$ 3. $48:72$ 4. $63:81$

5. $63:147$ 6. $8.1:9.9$ 7. $13:7.8$

8. $44.8:39.2$ 9. $\dfrac{1}{4}:\dfrac{3}{4}$ 10. $\dfrac{3}{8}:\dfrac{1}{2}$ 11. $2\dfrac{1}{4}:1\dfrac{3}{4}$

12. $4\dfrac{1}{2}:1\dfrac{2}{5}$ 13. $56\,\text{p}:80\,\text{p}$ 14. $42\,\text{p}:63\,\text{p}$

15. £120 : £15   16. £18 : £42

17. $40\,\text{cm}:130\,\text{cm}$ 18. $52\,\text{m}:78\,\text{m}$

19. $8.8\,\text{m}:24.2\,\text{m}$ 20. $42\,\text{km}:63\,\text{km}$

21. $5\,\text{mm}:2\,\text{cm}$ 22. $2\,\text{m}:55\,\text{cm}$

23. $150\,\text{cm}:3\,\text{m}$ 24. $4.2\,\text{m}:6000\,\text{cm}$

25. $650\,\text{cm}^3:1\dfrac{1}{2}\,\text{litres}$ 26. $72\,\text{p}:£2.16$

27. £8.40 : 42 p   28. $1500\,\text{mm}:2\,\text{m}$

29. $30\,\text{min}:2\,\text{h}$ 30. $2\dfrac{1}{4}\,\text{h}:5\,\text{h}$

31. $3\,\text{h}:48\,\text{min}$ 32. $245\,\text{min}:70\,\text{min}$

33. $1.5\,\text{kg}:500\,\text{g}$ 34. $1750\,\text{g}:3\,\text{kg}$

35. $49\,\text{g}:108\,\text{g}$ 36. $5.4\,\text{kg}:7.2\,\text{kg}.$

Which ratio is the greater?

37. $4:5$ or $8:9$ 38. $9:2$ or $7:3$

39. $4:3$ or $10:7$ 40. $14:9$ or $23:16.$

Which ratio is the smaller?

41. $3:4$ or $5:7$ 42. $7:8$ or $14:15$

43. $9:5$ or $26:17$ 44. $7:3$ or $20:9.$

Fill in the blanks in the following:

45. $\dfrac{2}{5}=\dfrac{}{20}=\dfrac{14}{}$ 46. $\dfrac{3}{7}=\dfrac{12}{}=\dfrac{}{56}$

47. $\dfrac{14}{13}=\dfrac{}{39}=\dfrac{70}{}$ 48. $\dfrac{7}{11}=\dfrac{56}{}=\dfrac{}{121}$

49. $\dfrac{}{9} = \dfrac{12}{27} = \dfrac{60}{}$

50. $\dfrac{7}{} = \dfrac{49}{56} = \dfrac{}{168}.$

51. Increase £10 in the ratio $5:2$.

52. Increase £5.60 in the ratio $13:8$.

53. Increase 588 cm in the ratio $12:7$.

54. Increase 15.3 m in the ratio $4:3$.

55. Increase 165 g in the ratio $9:5$.

56. Decrease £16.36 in the ratio $3:4$.

57. Decrease 84 p in the ratio $7:12$.

58. Decrease 323 mm in the ratio $6:19$.

59. Decrease 28 km in the ratio $5:8$.

60. Decrease 39.1 kg in the ratio $12:17$.

61. In a mixed class of 32 there are 14 boys. Find the ratio of boys to girls.

62. In a year group there are 216 boys and 288 girls. Find the ratio of girls to boys.

63. There are 1920 pupils in a school of whom 864 are boys. Find the ratio of:
(a) the number of boys to the number of girls
(b) the number of girls to the number of pupils.

64. John earns £200 per week while Jim earns £1000 per calendar month. Find the ratio of their yearly earnings.

65. A salesman spends $3\frac{1}{2}$ hours of his working day of $10\frac{1}{2}$ hours travelling. Find the ratio of:
(a) the time he is driving to the time he is not driving
(b) the time he is not driving to the length of his working day.

66. The number of children receiving free meals in a school increases from 161 to 184. In what ratio have the number of free meals increased?

67. The population of a village rose from 153 to 238. In what ratio did the population increase?

68. The air fare between two American cities is £545 at high season and £436 at low season. Find the ratio of these fares.

69. Find the ratio of the area of Wales, which is 7450 square miles, to the area of Scotland, which is 30 396 square miles.

70. Find the ratio of the area of Northern Ireland (5420 square miles) to that of the Republic of Ireland (27 100 square miles).

71. Find the ratio of the length of the River Seine, 768 km, to the length of the River Loire, 972 km.

72. Find the ratio of the areas of two squares whose sides are 2 cm and 3 cm.

73. A joint of frozen pork, weighing 2200 g, loses 88 g when thawed. In what ratio is its weight reduced?

74. A child sleeps $10\frac{1}{2}$ hours every day. Find the ratio of the time he is awake to the time he sleeps.

75. A boy is 12 years old now and his father is 42 years old. Find:
(a) the ratio of their present ages
(b) the ratio of their ages in 3 years' time.

76. A mother is 56 years old now and her daughter is 24. Find the ratio of their ages (a) now, (b) 12 years ago.

77. One car travels at 50 miles per hour while another travels at 1 mile per minute. Find the ratio of their speeds.

78. A woman's gross pay is £142 while her deductions amount to £42.60. Find the ratio of her deductions to her net pay.

79. A record shop increases its stock of records in the ratio 7:6. If its original stock was 2166 records, find:
(a) the total new stock
(b) the increase in the number of records.

80. The population of a rural area decreased from 2091 to 1845. In what ratio did the population decrease?

81. When the price of petrol increases in the ratio 6:5 a motorist reduces his mileage in the ratio 9:11. Find the ratio in which his petrol costs change.

82. When the price of tobacco increases in the ratio 9:7 a smoker reduces his consumption in the ratio 2:3. Find the ratio in which his smoking costs change.

83. In a sale goods are reduced by one-fifth. In what ratio are the prices reduced?

84. A man earns £12 480 in a year and spends £10 560. Find the ratio of:
(a) his income to his expenditure
(b) his savings to his income.

85. The following recipe will make 7 kg of marmalade: 2 kg oranges, 4 kg sugar, 1 lemon, 1 litre water. What quantities would be required to make 63 kg of marmalade?

86. The following recipe will make sufficient swiss roll for six people:

120 g flour, 125 g castor sugar, 2 eggs, 2 tablespoons jam. What quantities would be required to make sufficient swiss roll for 63 people?

87. The hours a man worked increased in the ratio $9:8$ and the hourly rate he was paid increased in the ratio $7:6$. In what ratio does his income increase?

88. The hours a woman worked increased in the ratio $13:10$ but her hourly rate of pay decreased in the ratio $8:9$. Was she better or worse off, and in what ratio?

89. A shopkeeper reduced the price of every article in his shop by 25 p in the £. What would be the new price of an article previously selling for £5.96?

90. A shopkeeper reduced the price of every article in her shop by 20 p in the £. What would be the original price of an article she now sold for £12.28?

REPRESENTATIVE FRACTION

The scale of a map is often given as a ratio. For example the current Ordnance Survey maps in most common use are in the ratio $1:50\,000$. This means that 1 cm on the map represents 50 000 cm or 500 m on the ground. Any two places on the map which are 5.5 cm apart will be 5.5×500 m = 2750 m = 2.75 km apart on the ground. Conversely any places which are 5.45 km apart on the ground will be:

$$\frac{5.45 \text{ km}}{50\,000} = \frac{5.45 \times 1000 \times 100 \text{ cm}}{50\,000}$$

$$= 10.9 \text{ cm apart on the map}$$

The fraction $\dfrac{1}{50\,000}$ is called the *representative fraction*, or RF of the map.

EXAMPLE 7   The RF of a map is $\dfrac{1}{50\,000}$. Find the distance in kilometres between two villages which are 14.4 cm apart on the map.

1 cm represents 50 000 cm

i.e.   1 cm represents 500 m

i.e.   1 cm represents 0.5 km

∴   14.4 cm represents 14.4×0.5 km = 7.2 km.

The distance between the villages is therefore 7.2 km.

EXAMPLE 8   The area of a lake is 4.5 square kilometres. What area will represent the lake on a map whose RF is $\dfrac{1}{50\,000}$?

50 000 cm is represented on the map by 1 cm

i.e.   0.5 km is represented on the map by 1 cm

∴   1 km is represented on the map by 2 cm

i.e.   1 km² is represented on the map by
2 × 2 cm² = 4 cm²

∴   4.5 km² is represented on the map by
4 × 4.5 cm² = 18 cm²

The area representing the lake on the map will therefore be 18 cm².

EXERCISE 43

1.   The scale of a map is 1 cm represents 1 km. Find its RF.

2.   The scale of a map is 1 cm represents 400 m. Find its RF.

3.   The scale of a map is 20 cm to 1 km. Find its RF.

4.   The plan of a house is 1 cm to 2 m. Find the RF of the plan. Find the length and breadth of the lounge on the plan if it measures 6 m by 4 m.

5.   The plan of a house is 1 cm to $2\frac{1}{2}$ m. Find the RF of the plan. Find the dimensions of a room which measures 1.6 cm by 2.4 cm on the plan.

6.   The plan of a house has an RF of $\dfrac{1}{50}$. Find the dimensions, on the plan, of a room which measures 5.5 m by 4 m.

7.   The scale of a map is 1 : 10 000. What area in square kilometres is represented by 1 cm² on the map?

8.   The RF of a map is $\dfrac{1}{50\,000}$. What area on a map (in square centimetres) represents a farm of area 8 square kilometres?

9.   The scale of a map is 1 : 1 000 000. Find, in square kilometres, the area of a stretch of water which has an area of 8.46 cm² on the map.

10. Two landmarks are found to be 132 mm apart on a map whose scale is 1 : 30 000. How many kilometres separate them?

11. The area of a pond is 53 m^2 and on a map it has an area of 0.53 cm^2. Find the RF of the map.

12. On a map a reservoir is represented by an area of 8.52 cm^2. If the scale of the map is $1:500\,000$, find the area of the reservoir in hectares. (1 hectare = 1000 square metres.)

13. The distance between two towns is 26 miles. Find the distance between these towns in centimetres on a map with RF $\dfrac{1}{50\,000}$. (1 mile = 1.61 km.)

14. On a map two schools are 140 mm apart. If the scale of the map is $1:20\,000$, find their distance apart (a) in kilometres, (b) in miles. (1 km = 0.621 mile.)

15. A three hundred acre farm is shown on a map. If the RF of the map is $\dfrac{1}{50\,000}$, find the area in square centimetres representing it on the map. (1 hectare = 2.471 acres.)

PROPORTIONAL PARTS

If a father divides £10 between his two children giving £7 to one and £3 to the other, we can consider the £10 as having 10 parts, of which he gives 7 to one child and 3 to the other. We say that he has divided the money between his children in the ratio $7:3$.

Conversely if we have a 45 cm length of copper tube and wish to divide it into three lengths which are in the ratio $2:3:4$, we think of the tube as having $2+3+4$ or 9 parts, each part being $\dfrac{45}{9}$ cm = 5 cm long.

The three pieces of tube will then have lengths 10 cm (2 parts), 15 cm (3 parts) and 20 cm (4 parts) respectively.

EXAMPLE 9   Divide £840 between A, B and C in the ratio $5:7:9$.

Consider the £840 to be divided into $5+7+9$ i.e. 21 equal parts.

Then   one part $= £\dfrac{840}{21} = £40.$

$\therefore$ A's share $= £5 \times 40 = £200$

B's share $= £7 \times 40 = £280$

and C's share $= £9 \times 40 = £360$

EXERCISE 44

1. Divide £42 in the ratio 4:3.

2. Divide 55 p in the ratio 2:3.

3. Divide 54 cm in the ratio 7:11.

4. Divide 3.6 m in the ratio 4:5.

5. Divide 20 km in the ratio 3:7.

6. Divide £66 in the ratio 2:4:5.

7. Divide 70 p in the ratio 2:3:5.

8. Divide 156 mm in the ratio 5:4:3.

9. Divide 322 cm in the ratio 2:5:7.

10. Divide 450 g in the ratio 5:7:13.

11. Divide £39 in the ratio $\frac{1}{2}:\frac{1}{3}:\frac{1}{4}$.

12. Divide 88 p in the ratio $\frac{1}{2}:\frac{1}{4}:\frac{1}{6}$.

13. Divide 960 g in the ratio 1.5:2:2.5.

14. Divide 154 cm in the ratio 0.5:0.8:0.9.

15. Divide 154 cm in the ratio 8:6.4:3.2.

16. Find two numbers whose sum is 144 and whose ratio is 9:7.

17. Find two numbers whose sum is 104 and whose ratio is 4:9.

18. Find two numbers whose difference is 15 and whose ratio is 4:3.

19. Find two numbers whose difference is 44 and whose ratio is 7:11.

20. The length, width and height of a room are in the ratio 4:3:2. If the sum of all three quantities is 11.25 m, find the dimensions of the room.

21. Divide 98 p between three girls, Alison, Beryl and Chris in the ratio 2:5:7.

22. Divide an 80 cm rod into three parts in the ratio 4:7:9.

23. The sides of a triangle are in the ratio 5:6:7. If the distance around the triangle is 63 cm, find the length of each side.

24. Three people A, B and C enter into partnership in a business. They agree to find capital in the ratio 4:5:6. If C puts up £14 400, calculate (a) the total capital required, (b) how much B invests in the business.

25. A quantity of coal weighing 36.75 t is to be carried by three lorries in the ratio 7:5:9. How much will each lorry carry?

26. Two youth clubs are to receive a grant from the local authority in proportion to their respective memberships. If one has 338 members and the other 494, how would a grant of £2560 be divided between them?

27. If $A:B = 3:4$ and $B:C = 2:5$, find $A:B:C$.

28. If $X:Y = 4:5$ and $Y:Z = 3:4$, find $X:Y:Z$.

29. If $a:b = 3:5$ and $b:c = 3:5$, find $a:b:c$.

30. If $p:q = \frac{1}{2}:\frac{1}{3}$ and $q:r = \frac{3}{4}:\frac{1}{4}$, find $p:q:r$.

31. Divide £55 between A, B and C so that A's share is twice B's share and three times C's share.

32. Divide £250 between A, B and C so that B's share is one-half of A's, and C's share is one-third of B's share.

33. Profits in a business amounting to £957 are to be divided between the partners John, Joan and Jim in the ratio of the capital they invested. If John invested £1320, Joan £1056, and Jim £528, how much does Joan receive?

34. An alloy consists of copper and zinc in the ratio 5:7. What weight of copper will be required to add to 931 kg of zinc? How much alloy will this give?

35. An alloy consists of zinc, copper and tin in the ratio of 2:7:4. Find the amount of each metal in 65 g of alloy.

DIRECT PROPORTION

If   1 jar of jam costs 80 p

then   3 jars of jam will cost $3 \times 80\,\text{p} = 240\,\text{p}$

and   7 jars of jam will cost $7 \times 80\,\text{p} = 560\,\text{p}$

Since the total cost increases as the number of jars increases, the cost is said to increase in *direct proportion* to the number of jars bought.

EXAMPLE 10 If a car uses 3 gallons of petrol for a journey of 162 miles, how far will it travel on 8 gallons?

On 3 gallons the car will travel 162 miles.

$\therefore$ on 1 gallon it will travel $\dfrac{162}{3}$ miles $= 54$ miles

$\therefore$ on 8 gallons it will travel 54×8 miles
$= 432$ miles

EXAMPLE 11 If five coaches are required to transport 260 supporters to a football match, how many similar coaches would be required to transport 1092 supporters?

260 supporters require 5 coaches

$\therefore$ 1 supporter requires $\dfrac{5}{260}$ coaches

then 1092 supporters will require $\dfrac{5}{260} \times 1092$ coaches

$\therefore$ 1092 supporters require 21 coaches.

EXERCISE 45

1. If 12 bars of soap cost £8.52, how much will 20 cost?

2. If 5 packets of tea cost £3.35, how much will 12 cost?

3. Twenty-seven articles cost £4.59. Find the cost of 44 at the same rate.

4. Thirty-five packets of sweets cost £12.60. Find the cost of 53 similar packets.

5. If 7 bananas cost £1.26 find the cost of 32.

6. If 12 oranges cost £1.68 find the cost of 25.

7. A man earns £288 by working for 36 hours. How much would he earn by working for 44 hours at the same rate?

8. A car travels $192\frac{1}{2}$ miles on 5 gallons of petrol. How far will it travel on 8 gallons?

9. A car requires 7 gallons of petrol for a journey of 245 miles. How many gallons will be required for a journey of 455 miles?

10. A small car will run for 266 km on 19 litres of petrol. How far will it run on 32 litres?

11. A motorcycle requires 14 litres of petrol to cover 308 km. How many litres will be required for a journey of 341 km?

12. A hotel charges £259 per person per week. What would be the charge for 16 days at the same rate?

13. The airfare for a 1350 mile flight is £202.50. What would be the fare for a flight of 3440 miles at the same rate?

14. The cost of publishing a book with 105 pages is £3.36. How many pages could be expected in a book costing £7.52 if the cost per page is considered constant?

15. A television set cost £65.52 to hire for 7 months. How much would it cost to hire for 2 years?

16. A new candle which is 18 cm tall will burn for $4\frac{1}{2}$ hours. What height remains when it has been burning for 2 hours 40 minutes?

17. If 544 people attend a concert, the takings amount to £3916.80. How many attended on the following evening when the takings amounted to £2858.40? (Assume that all seats were sold at the same price.)

18. Mr Brown paid £319.60 in rates on his house which had a rateable value of £340. If he moved to a new house with a rateable value of £516, how much would he expect to pay in rates?

19. An alloy is made by mixing copper with lead in the ratio $7:9$ by mass. What mass of lead would be required to mix with 266 kg of copper, and what mass of alloy would result?

20. Railway freight charges were increased from $7\frac{1}{2}$ p to $9\frac{1}{2}$ p for each article dispatched from a factory. What is the new freight charge for an order which used to cost £19.20?

21. It used to cost 15 p each to send certain articles by post. If the cost of posting a parcel containing a given number of articles increases from £22.20 to £25.90, find the new cost of posting a single article.

22. If three-sevenths of a load of hay has a mass of 1728 kg, what is the mass of four-ninths of the same load?

23. If five-twelfths of a sum of money is £24.50, what is four-sevenths of the same sum?

24. If fifteen machines cost £9465, what would be the cost of eighteen similar machines?

25. It costs £253.75 to carpet a rectangular lounge measuring 3.5 metres by 5 metres. How much would it cost to cover the dining room measuring 2.5 metres by 3 metres with a similar carpet?

INVERSE PROPORTION

Suppose it takes 7 men 60 days to lay a section of motorway. The same section would be laid by:

1 man in 420 days
2 men in 210 days
3 men in 140 days
4 men in 105 days
5 men in 84 days
6 men in 70 days
7 men in 60 days and so on.

Selecting two of these lines at random and rewriting:

                 3 men will lay the section in 140 days
and   7 men will lay the section in 60 days

The ratio of the number of men is $3:7$ or $\dfrac{3}{7}$ and the ratio of the number of days they take is:

$$\frac{140}{60} = \frac{7}{3}$$

Thus if the number of men employed is increased in the ratio $7:3$, the time taken decreases in the ratio $3:7$. This is an example of *inverse proportion*. Two quantities are said to vary inversely or be in inverse proportion if an increase (or decrease) in one causes a corresponding decrease (or increase) in the other.

EXAMPLE 12   If it takes 64 men 42 hours to assemble a light aeroplane, how long would it take 21 men?

Method 1   If the number of men is reduced in the ratio $\dfrac{21}{64}$, the time they will take will be increased in the ratio $\dfrac{64}{21}$.

$\therefore$ Time taken $= 42 \times \dfrac{64}{21}$ hours $= 128$ hours

Method 2   Arrange the data:

NO. OF MEN	TIME TAKEN IN HOURS
64	42
21	x

Since the values are in inverse proportion

$$\frac{64}{21} = \frac{x}{42}$$

i.e. $21x = 64 \times 42$

$$\therefore \quad x = \frac{64 \times 42}{21} = 128$$

$\therefore$ Time taken $= 128$ hours

Method 3 (The unitary method). If 64 men take 42 hours to assemble the aeroplane, then 1 man takes 64×42 hours to assemble the aeroplane.

$$\therefore \quad 21 \text{ men take } \frac{64 \times 42}{21} \text{ hours} = 128 \text{ hours}$$

EXERCISE 46

1. A coach takes 2 hours to make a journey when travelling at 60 mph. How long would the journey take if the coach travelled at 40 mph?

2. A car takes 6 hours to make a journey when travelling at 70 mph. What would be its average speed if it took 5 hours for the same journey?

3. If it takes 21 men 4 days to mark out an athletics stadium, how long would it take 12 men to do the same job?

4. A small boat has sufficient food to last its crew of 12 for 9 days. If it rescues six people from the sea, how long will the same food last?

5. A school boiler which consumes 0.75 t of fuel a day has a 12 day supply. If cold weather causes the consumption to increase to 0.9 t a day, how many days will it last?

6. If it takes 360 square tiles of side 10 cm to cover a wall, how many of side 15 cm would be required to cover the same wall?

7. If the volume of a given mass of gas is 4.2 cm^3 when its pressure is 30 cm of mercury, find the volume when the pressure is increased to 36 cm of mercury. (Assume that volume and pressure are inversely related.)

8. When a box of chocolates is divided among 5 people they have 8 chocolates each. If the box was divided between 4 people, how many chocolates would each receive?

9. A fruit farmer employs 34 men to harvest his apples. If they take 9 days to do the job, how many men would be required to do the job in 6 days?

10. A factory requires 45 sewing machines to produce a given quantity of dresses in 22 days. How many machines would be required to produce the same number of dresses in 18 days?

11. My bookshelf will hold 360 books of average thickness 2 cm. How many copies of *National Geographic* will it hold if the average copy is 6 mm thick?

12. The average waiting time at a supermarket when 12 check-outs are available is 8 minutes. How many check-outs would be required to reduce the waiting time to 3 minutes?

13. A brass band and a theatre group receive equal grants from the local authority. The band has 44 members and receives the equivalent of £7 for each member, while the theatre group only receives the equivalent of £4 per member. How many members are there in the theatre group?

14. Water in a rectangular tank with a base area of $1.5 \, \text{m}^2$ is 24 cm deep. If it is run off into another rectangular tank of base area $1.2 \, \text{m}^2$, to what height will it rise?

15. If the cost of gas for heating 12 greenhouses for 5 days is £70, how many greenhouses could be heated for 4 days at the same cost?

16. A cog wheel with 60 cogs meshes with a cog wheel with 35 cogs. If the former makes 84 revolutions in a minute, how many does the other make?

17. Two gear wheels mesh together, one making 60 revolutions per minute and the other 80. If the smaller wheel has 30 teeth, how many teeth does the larger wheel have?

18. A boys' camp has enough stores to support 42 boys for 14 days. If 49 boys attend the camp how long will the stores last?

19. A ball of string may be cut into 45 pieces, each of length 28 cm. How many pieces 63 cm long could be cut from the same ball?

20. In a school 44 classrooms are required if each class size is 30 pupils. How many more classrooms would be required if all the class sizes are cut to 24?

COMPOUND PROPORTION

In simple proportion only two quantities are involved, but in compound proportion we are concerned with more than two quantities. It is often convenient to introduce special units, e.g. if 8 men work for 6 hours we could say that they have produced $8 \times 6 = 48$ man-hours' work, or if an aeroplane carries 120 passengers for 350 miles, the airline is able to charge for 120×350 passenger-miles.

EXAMPLE 13   If 6 men earn £360 for 12 hours' work, how much will 8 men earn for 20 hours' work at the same rate?

Method 1   Let us call 1 man working for 1 hour a man-hour.

Then 6×12 man-hours costs £360

i.e.   1 man-hour costs $£\dfrac{360}{6 \times 12} = £5$

∴ 8×20 man-hours will cost $£8 \times 20 \times 5 = £800$

i.e. 8 men working for 20 hours will earn £800.

Method 2   Question: Will 8 men earn more or less than 6?

Answer: More. Therefore multiply by $\dfrac{8}{6}$.

Question: Will a given number of men earn more or less in 20 hours than in 12 hours?

Answer: More. Therefore multiply by $\dfrac{20}{12}$.

i.e.   Amount earned by 8 men in 20 hours

$$= £360 \times \frac{8}{6} \times \frac{20}{12} = £800$$

EXERCISE 47

1. If 8 men earn £288 for 9 hours' work, how much will 11 men earn for 7 hours' work?

2. Six girls earn £90 for 5 hours' work. How much should 8 girls earn for 4 hours' work?

3. If 6 boys earn £300 in 5 days, how much will 4 boys earn in 12 days?

4. Eight gas heaters running for 4 hours cost £3.84. How much will nine heaters cost to run for 7 hours?

5. The income received by hiring 7 mixing machines for 8 days is £448. What would be the income if 4 machines were hired for 15 days?

6. In a packing department 16 women pack 1568 boxes in 7 hours. How many boxes should be packed by 21 women in 6 hours?

7. If a workforce of 15 is required to produce 945 articles in 7 hours, what workforce is required to produce 864 articles in 8 hours?

8. The cost of transporting 8 t of goods 30 miles is £320. How many tonnes of goods could be expected to be transported 100 miles for £600?

9. In a certain school 80 teachers are required if each teaches a 34 period week. How many teachers will be required if the teaching week is reduced to 32 periods?

10. If a field contains enough grass to graze 36 sheep for 18 days, how many sheep could graze a field 3 times as large for 8 days?

11. A bank charges £21 for a loan of £300 for 6 months. What would be the charge for a loan of £5000 for 14 months?

12. Eighteen college staff can enrol 1980 students in 5 hours. How many staff are required to enrol 1056 students in 4 hours?

13. The cost of petrol for a 120 km journey for a car which travels 20 km on each litre of petrol is £2.40. What would be the cost for a 300 km journey in a car which travels 15 km on each litre?

14. Last quarter my electricity bill was £60 when I used 1200 units of electricity, each unit costing 5 p. This quarter I intend cutting my use by $\frac{1}{5}$ since the cost of electricity has increased by 1 p per unit. What should my next electricity bill be?

15. In a school canteen the food bill for a week when they are catering for 380 pupils is £760. How much should it rise or fall if the cost of a meal increases by 25% while the number of pupils served falls by 100?

PERCENTAGES

Per cent means per hundred, e.g. 12 per cent means 12 per hundred. If 12 per cent of the pupils in a school are absent, then for every 100 pupils on the register 12 of them are absent. If there are 1400 i.e. 14×100 pupils in the school, $14 \times 12 = 168$ will be absent.

In mathematics we are always looking for shorter ways of writing things and especially for symbols instead of words. Instead of the 'per cent' we write %. Therefore 12% and 12 per cent have exactly the same meaning.

It follows that 12% can be written in fraction form as $\dfrac{12}{100}$ or $\dfrac{3}{25}$

i.e. 12% is equivalent to $\dfrac{3}{25}$.

Percentages are fractions with a denominator of 100

e.g. $\qquad \dfrac{3}{20} = \dfrac{15}{100}$ or 15%

Percentages may be expressed as fractions and fractions are easily converted into percentages.

A percentage is converted into a fraction by dividing by 100 and simplifying

e.g. $\qquad 20\% = \dfrac{20}{100} = \dfrac{1}{5} = 0.2$

and $\qquad 65\% = \dfrac{65}{100} = \dfrac{13}{20} = 0.65$

A fraction is converted into a percentage by multiplying by 100

e.g. $\qquad \dfrac{3}{5} = \dfrac{3}{5} \times 100\% = 60\%$

and $$\frac{17}{20} = \frac{17}{20} \times 100\% = 85\%$$

It is only a short step from the above to 'Express 35 cm as a percentage of 2 m'.

The first quantity as a fraction of the second is $\frac{35}{200}$ (taking great care to see that both are in the same units).

Then $$\frac{35}{200} = \frac{35}{200} \times 100\% = 17\frac{1}{2}\%$$

EXERCISE 48

Express the following as percentages:

1. $\frac{1}{2}, \frac{1}{4}, \frac{1}{8}, \frac{3}{8}, \frac{5}{8}$

2. $\frac{7}{8}, \frac{1}{3}, \frac{2}{3}, \frac{9}{8}, \frac{17}{8}$

3. $\frac{1}{5}, \frac{2}{5}, \frac{4}{5}, \frac{6}{5}, \frac{8}{5}$

4. $\frac{11}{20}, \frac{3}{25}, \frac{5}{6}, \frac{9}{20}, \frac{17}{50}$

5. $\frac{29}{25}, 1\frac{1}{3}, 2\frac{9}{10}, 1\frac{1}{10}, 1\frac{7}{8}$

6. $0.25, 0.35, 0.47, 0.06, 0.72$

7. $1.23, 2, 3.04, 0.655, 12.24.$

Express the following percentages as (a) common fractions in their lowest terms, (b) decimals:

8. $25\%, 50\%, 75\%, 40\%, 60\%$

9. $55\%, 48\%, 64\%, 76\%, 35\%$

10. $12\frac{1}{2}\%, 37\frac{1}{2}\%, 62\frac{1}{2}\%, 87\frac{1}{2}\%, 16\frac{2}{3}\%.$

11. If 32% of the boys in a year group take woodwork, what percentage do not?

12. A man spends 43% of his income on household expenses, 28% on pleasure, saves 8% and spends the remainder on his car. What percentage is spent on his car?

13. If 72% of the cost of a cigarette is tax, how much is not?

14. An object is 43% animal, 29% vegetable and the remainder is mineral. What percentage is mineral?

15. The cost of running a car is 28% petrol, 35% road tax, insurance and repairs, and the remainder depreciation. What percentage accounts for depreciation?

16. Marmalade consists of 28% fruit, 58% sugar and the remainder water. Find the percentage of water.

17. At an election 31% vote Labour, 31% vote Conservative and the remainder for the SDP. What percentage vote for the SDP?

Express the first quantity as a percentage of the second:

18. (a) 5, 20   (b) 4, 40   (c) 16, 64   (d) 50, 25
    (e) 15, 60

19. (a) 12 cm, 60 cm   (b) 33 cm, 1 m   (c) 4 m, 3 m
    (d) 400 m, 1 km   (e) 243 mm, 30 cm

20. (a) 24 cm^2, 96 cm^2 (b) 200 mm^2, 40 cm^2
    (c) 1000 cm^2, 1 m^2 (d) 550 cm^3, 1 litre
    (e) 844 cm^3, 2 litres

21. (a) 1600 g, 2 kg   (b) 2.64 kg, 8.8 kg
    (c) 850 kg, 1 t   (d) $157\frac{1}{2}$ g, 450 g
    (e) 36 g, 50 g.

Find the value of:

22. (a) 30% of 8 m   (b) 65% of 5 cm
    (c) 85% of 2.5 km

23. (a) $12\frac{1}{2}$% of 720 g   (b) $66\frac{2}{3}$% of 369 kg
    (c) 125% of 36 g

24. (a) 37% of 84   (b) $16\frac{2}{3}$% of 159 cm
    (c) $58\frac{1}{2}$% of 44 m.

25. In a third year 52% of the 250 pupils study French. How many do not study French?

26. Deductions from a man's wage amount to 40%. What is his wage after deductions if he earns £320?

27. In a biology test a girl scores 26 marks out of 40. What percentage is this?

28. The constituents of gunpowder are: nitre 75%, charcoal 15% and sulphur 10%. How many kilograms of gunpowder may be made from 12 kg of charcoal?

29. In an election 47% of the electorate voted Labour, 15% Conservative and the remainder for the Nationalist candidate. If there were 64 500 voters, how many voted for the Nationalist?

30. In a local election 56% of the electorate voted Conservative, 37% Labour and the remainder Liberal. If 44 400 are eligible to vote, how many more votes did the Conservative candidate receive than the Liberal?

31. In a form 75% are boys and 9 are girls. How many pupils are there in the form?

32. In a year group 65% are girls and 84 are boys. How many girls are there?

33. In a form of 30, 9 study cookery. What percentage do not?

34. If 50% of a number is 20, find the number.

35. If 20% of a number is 25, find the number.

36. If 60% of a sum of money is £3.60, find the sum of money.

37. If 75% of a sum of money is £7.20, find the sum of money.

38. If 35% of a sum of money is £43.40, find the sum of money.

39. In a family 40% are males. What is the smallest number of females in the family?

40. A house was sold for £60 000 which was 96% of what it cost to build. How much did it cost to build?

41. In a sale a shopkeeper reduced his prices by 30 p in the pound. What percentage was this?

42. In a sale an article was marked down from £21.40 to £18.19. What percentage reduction was this?

43. In a sale a coat was marked down from £134 to £87.10. What percentage reduction was this?

44. A piece of frozen fish lost 4% of its mass when thawed. If its mass was 1.44 kg when thawed, what was its mass when frozen?

45. A packet of cornflakes was full when it left the factory but 'settling' caused the volume taken by the cornflakes to reduce by 8%. If the volume of the packet was 3000 cm^3, find the volume taken by the cornflakes when they had settled.

46. In end of term examinations a pupil scored a total of 572 marks out of a possible 800. Express this result as a percentage.

47. In an examination a pupil gained 221 marks out of a possible 340. What percentage is this?

48. In a test a boy gained 85% of the marks. How many marks did he receive if the total possible was 460?

49. A girl sat three mathematics papers and had an average mark of 66%. If she scored 52 out of a hundred in the first paper and 73 out of a hundred in the second, how many did she score out of 100 in the third?

50. A broker charges $1\frac{1}{2}$% commission on shares he sells. If he sells 5420 shares at £4.40 each for a client, calculate his commission.

PERCENTAGE CHANGE

When the government announces that prices have increased by 10% it means that for every £100 we previously needed to buy goods and services we now need £110. For example:

A car which cost £15 000 would increase to

$$£15\,000 \times \frac{110}{100} = £16\,500$$

A can of fruit which cost £1.40 would increase to

$$£1.40 \times \frac{110}{100} = £1.54$$

A holiday which cost £1250 would rise to

$$£1250 \times \frac{110}{100} = £1375$$

If the original price is represented by 100, the new price is represented by 110, i.e. the new price may be calculated by multiplying the original cost by $\frac{110}{100}$ which is called the *multiplying factor*.

Similarly if a car depreciates by 20% during its first year, every £100 of value has decreased by £20 to £80, i.e. the new value is found by multiplying the purchase price by the multiplying factor $\frac{80}{100}$.

If the car was bought for £20 000 it would be worth:

$$£20\,000 \times \frac{80}{100} = £16\,000 \qquad \text{after one year}$$

EXERCISE 49

1. What multiplying factor increases a number by:
   (a) 20%   (b) 50%   (c) 35%   (d) 120%
   (e) 200%?

2. What multiplying factor decreases a number by:
   (a) 20%   (b) 60%   (c) 12%   (d) 35%
   (e) 75%?

3. Increase the given numbers by the given percentage:
   (a) 100, 30% (b) 240, 60%
   (c) 30, 80% (d) 66, $33\frac{1}{3}$%
   (e) 64, $12\frac{1}{2}$%.

4. Decrease the given numbers by the given percentage:
   (a) 200, 40% (b) 175, 30%
   (c) 21, $66\frac{2}{3}$% (d) 64, $12\frac{1}{2}$%.

5. The price of a watch marked £60 rises by 12%. Find its new price.

6. A man's weekly wage of £550 rises by 15%. Find his new wage.

7. A girl's weight increased by 8% on holiday. If she weighed 65 kg before she went, how much did she weigh on her return?

8. A boy's height increased by 20% between his twelfth and fourteenth birthdays. If he was 145 cm on his twelfth birthday, how tall was he on his fourteenth?

9. Water increases in volume by 4% when frozen. Find the volume of 525 cm³ of water when converted into ice.

10. The water rate on a property is 18% higher this year than last year. If it was £160 last year, what will it be this year?

11. A girl is 25% taller now than she was 3 years ago. If she is 160 cm now, how tall was she 3 years ago?

12. The number of children attending school in the county of Peaceshire is 6% fewer this year than last year. If 63 200 were attending school last year, how many are attending this year?

13. In a sale the price of an article marked at £74 is reduced by 15%. What is its sale price?

14. A car, bought for £16 000, loses 72% of its value over a 5 year period. Find its value after 5 years.

15. A woman's height decreased by 5% between her fiftieth and seventy-fifth birthdays. If her height was 1.82 m when she was fifty, how tall was she 25 years later?

16. A man's weight increased by 63% between his twentieth and fortieth birthdays. At twenty he weighed 48 kg. How much did he weigh on his fortieth birthday?

17. When making a model stool a boy estimated that he had 72% of the wood he started with in the finished model. If the model weighed 2.52 kg, what weight of wood did he start with?

18. A retailer sold an article for £54 thus gaining $12\frac{1}{2}$% on the amount it cost him. How much did it cost him?

19. The percentage of staff in a school decreased by 5%. If 114 staff remain, how many left?

20. The widening of a road results in the garden of a house being reduced in area by 35%. If the area of the garden is $546\,\text{m}^2$ after widening, what was its original area?

PERCENTAGE PROFIT AND LOSS

When a retailer buys goods and is able to sell them at a higher price, a profit is made, which is the difference between the selling price (SP) and the cost price (CP). The percentage profit made is always calculated by expressing the *profit as a percentage of the cost price*.

Thus   Percentage profit $= \dfrac{\text{profit}}{\text{cost price}} \times 100$

i.e.   % Profit $= \dfrac{\text{SP} - \text{CP}}{\text{CP}} \times 100$

Similarly   % Loss $= \dfrac{\text{loss}}{\text{CP}} \times 100$ i.e.   % Loss $= \dfrac{\text{CP} - \text{SP}}{\text{CP}} \times 100$

EXAMPLE 1   A retailer bought a clock for £55 and sold it for £77. Find his percentage profit.

Profit $=$ SP $-$ CP

$=$ £77 $-$ £55

$=$ £22

% Profit $= \dfrac{\text{profit}}{\text{CP}} \times 100$

$= \dfrac{£22}{£55} \times 100$

i.e.   Profit $= 40\%$

EXAMPLE 2   A retailer bought a can of fruit for 80 p and sold it at a profit of 25%. Find the selling price.

Method 1   Profit is 25% or $\dfrac{25}{100}$ of the CP

i.e.   Profit $= 80 \times \dfrac{25}{100}$ p

$= 20\,\text{p}$

$\therefore$ SP $=$ CP $+$ profit

$= 80\,\text{p} + 20\,\text{p}$

$=$ £1

127

Method 2

$$SP = CP + \frac{25}{100} CP$$

$$= \frac{125}{100} CP$$

$$= CP \times \frac{125}{100}$$

$$= 80 \times \frac{125}{100} p$$

$$= 100 p$$

$$= £1$$

In general terms, if the profit is *P*%

$$SP = CP \times \frac{(100 + P)}{100}$$

For example if CP = £5 and profit is 35%

$$SP = £5 \times \frac{(100 + 35)}{100}$$

$$= £5 \times \frac{135}{100}$$

$$= £6.75$$

EXAMPLE 3   Linda buys a record for £6 but decides she does not like it very much so she sells it to a friend at a loss of 15%. How much does the friend pay for it?

Method 1

Loss is 15% or $\frac{15}{100}$ of the cost price

i.e. Loss $= £6 \times \dfrac{15}{100}$

$$= £0.90$$

$\therefore$ SP $=$ CP $-$ loss

$$= £6 - £0.90$$

$$= £5.10$$

$$SP = CP - \frac{15}{100}CP$$

$$= \frac{85}{100}CP$$

$$= CP \times \frac{85}{100}$$

$$= £6 \times \frac{85}{100}$$

$$= £5.10$$

In general terms, if the loss is $L\%$

$$SP = CP \times \frac{(100-L)}{100}$$

For example if $CP = £36$ and loss is 45%

$$SP = £36 \times \frac{(100-45)}{100}$$

$$= £36 \times \frac{55}{100}$$

$$= £19.80$$

EXAMPLE 4   When a radio cassette recorder is sold for £33.60 the shopkeeper makes a profit of 40%. Find the cost price.

Method 1   The percentage profit (or loss) is always on the cost price.

$$\text{Since} \quad SP = CP \times \frac{(100+P)}{100}$$

$$£33.60 = CP \times \frac{(100+40)}{100}$$

$$= CP \times \frac{140}{100}$$

i.e. $£33.60 \times \dfrac{100}{140} = CP$ $\left(\text{multiplying each side}\right.$

$$\left. \text{by } \frac{100}{140}\right)$$

or $\quad CP = £33.60 \times \dfrac{100}{140}$

$\qquad\qquad = £24$

Method 2 If the cost price is 100 p, the selling price will be

$$100 \times \dfrac{140}{100}\text{p} = 140\,\text{p}$$

i.e. the cost price is $\dfrac{100}{140}$ of the selling price

$\therefore \quad CP = £33.60 \times \dfrac{100}{140}$

$\qquad\qquad = £24$

EXAMPLE 5   A second hand car dealer sells a car for £1840. If this means that he has suffered a loss of 8%, how much did he pay for it?

Method 1

$$SP = CP \times \dfrac{(100 - L)}{100}$$

i.e. $\quad £1840 = CP \times \dfrac{(100 - 8)}{100}$

$\qquad\qquad\quad = CP \times \dfrac{92}{100}$

i.e. $\quad CP = £1840 \times \dfrac{100}{92}$

$\qquad\qquad = £2000$

Method 2 If the cost price is £100, the selling price will be

$$£100 \times \dfrac{92}{100} = £92$$

i.e. the cost price is $\dfrac{100}{92}$ of the selling price

$\therefore \quad CP = £1840 \times \dfrac{100}{92}$

$\qquad\qquad = £2000$

EXAMPLE 6

John Baker buys eight packs of towels at £35 per pack, each pack containing 25 towels. He is able to sell the towels at £1.96 each. Calculate (a) the total profit, (b) the percentage profit.

Cost of 8 packs at £35 per pack $= £8 \times 35$

$$= £280$$

Number of towels bought $= 8 \times 25$

$$= 200$$

Amount received by selling 200 towels at £1.96 each

$$= £1.96 \times 200$$

$$= £392$$

$\therefore$ Profit $=$ SP $-$ CP

$$= £392 - £280$$

$$= £112$$

% Profit $= \dfrac{\text{Profit}}{\text{CP}} \times 100$

$$= \dfrac{£112}{£280} \times 100$$

i.e. Profit $= 40\%$

EXERCISE 50

In each of the following write down the factor by which the cost price must be multiplied to give the selling price:

1. Profit 20%
2. Profit 50%
3. Profit 45%
4. Profit $33\frac{1}{3}\%$
5. Loss 20%
6. Loss 60%
7. Loss 75%
8. Loss $66\frac{2}{3}\%$
9. Profit 5%
10. Loss 12%.

In each of the following find the selling price:

11. CP £2, profit 20%
12. CP £10, loss 10%
13. CP £10, loss 25%
14. CP £16, profit 50%
15. CP £15, profit 30%
16. CP £300, profit 8%
17. CP £120, loss 60%
18. CP £7.50, loss 80%
19. CP £4.96, profit $12\frac{1}{2}\%$
20. CP £639, loss $33\frac{1}{3}\%$.

In each of the following write down the factor by which the selling price must be multiplied to give the cost price:

21. Profit 20%
22. Profit 50%
23. Profit 75%
24. Profit $66\frac{2}{3}$%
25. Loss 60%
26. Loss 10%
27. Loss 50%
28. Profit $12\frac{1}{2}$%
29. Loss $37\frac{1}{2}$%
30. Loss 15%.

In each of the following find the cost price:

31. SP £126, profit 5%
32. SP £80, profit 100%
33. SP £2.04, loss 40%
34. SP 18 p, loss $33\frac{1}{3}$%
35. SP £2.20, profit 10%
36. SP 63 p, loss 30%
37. SP £17.28, profit 60%
38. SP £7.69, loss 60%
39. SP £17, loss 15%
40. SP £336, profit 180%.

In each of the following find the percentage profit or loss:

41. CP £4, profit 60 p
42. CP £60, profit £12
43. CP £350, loss £42
44. CP £60, loss £15
45. CP £105, profit £63
46. CP £5.60, SP £7
47. CP £7.30, SP £9.49
48. CP £60, SP £102
49. CP £14.90, SP £26.82
50. CP £480, SP £540.

EXERCISE 51   MISCELLANEOUS EXAMPLES

1. A calculator is bought for £5 and sold at a loss of 40%. Find the selling price.

2. A bookseller buys a book for £8.50 and sells it for £15.30. Find the percentage profit.

3. A house bought for £48 000 is sold at a profit of 12%. Find the selling price.

4. Imported bicycles cost a dealer £110 and are sold at 35% profit. Find the selling price.

5. Six months after paying £8000 for a car the owner is forced to sell for £6560. Find the percentage loss.

6. Record albums sold at £9.80 result in a loss of 30% for the shopkeeper. How much did he pay for them?

7. A box of paints bought for £12 is sold at a profit of $22\frac{1}{2}\%$. Find the selling price.

8. Ray George made a loss of $16\frac{2}{3}\%$ by selling some potatoes for £6. How much did they cost him?

9. A silversmith sells silver for £264, thereby making 120% profit. How much did the silver cost him?

10. An art dealer bought a picture for £3500 and sold it at a profit of 80%. Find the selling price.

11. A discount store bought a suite of furniture for £1260 and sold it at a profit of $66\frac{2}{3}\%$. How much did they sell it for?

12. Ernie Pugh buys a greyhound for £360 and sells it at a loss of $12\frac{1}{2}\%$. How much does he lose?

13. A greengrocer buys a box of 150 Seville oranges for £13.50 and sells them at 14 p each. Find his percentage profit.

14. A scrap metal dealer buys lead for £72 and sells it for £132. Find his percentage profit.

15. By selling a picture for £2160 an antique dealer makes a profit of 80%. What did she pay for it?

16. By selling a quantity of gold for £11 340 a bullion dealer makes a profit of 110%. What did he pay for it?

17. Jane bought a necklace for £7.50 and sold it at a loss of 36%. How much did she lose?

18. If a second hand car dealer buys a car for £4600 and sells it at a loss of 15%, how much does he sell it for?

19. Dried fruit bought at £44 per 50 kg bag is sold at £1.21 per kilogram. Find the percentage profit.

20. Eggs are bought at the farm for £1.50 per tray and sold at 90 p per dozen. If a tray holds 36 eggs, find the percentage profit.

21. A retailer buys 100 articles for £180 and sells them at £2.40 each. Find the percentage profit.

22. A shopkeeper buys 300 articles for £1200 and sells them at £3.50 each. Find his percentage loss.

23. A shopkeeper buys an article and 'marks it up' so that he makes 80% profit on the cost price. If he allows 5% off the marked price for cash, find the cost price of an article he sells for £8.55 cash.

24. A garage allows 12% off the list price of a car when no car is offered in part-exchange. If the list price is calculated by adding 60% to the cost price, how much profit does the dealer make on a car costing him £12 000?

25. A herb bought at £25 per kilogram is sold at 3 p per gram. Find the percentage profit.

26. A builders' merchant allows a discount of $2\frac{1}{2}$% if payment is made within seven days. How much would I save by paying a bill totalling £768 immediately?

27. A small business made a profit of £8909 this year. If this was an increase of 18% over last year, how much profit was made last year?

28. The population of Bernshire increased by 5% last year but had decreased by 2% the previous year. If the population is 12 348 now, what was it (a) last year, (b) 2 years ago?

29. The local team's score was standing at 180 for 9 wickets when the last pair came together. If these two increased the total by 35%, find:
    (a) how many runs they put on for the last wicket
    (b) the innings score.

30. A tailor 'marks up' his suits to give a profit of 55%. In a sale he reduces all his prices by 10% which means that Joe Bloggs is able to save £18.60 on the suit he buys. Find:
    (a) the original marked price of the suit
    (b) the tailor's actual profit on the suit.

12

AREA AND VOLUME

AREA

The *area* of a plane figure is the amount of surface enclosed within its boundary lines. The total length of these boundary lines is called its *perimeter*.

In the metric system we have the metre as the standard unit of length, from which several other units follow. In the same way the square metre, which is the area contained within a square of side one metre, is the standard unit of area. The particular unit used depends on the amount of area we are measuring. Thus we might measure the area of the head of a screw in square millimetres (mm^2), the area of a page of this book in square centimetres (cm^2), the area of a roof in square metres (m^2) and the area of a country in square kilometres (km^2).

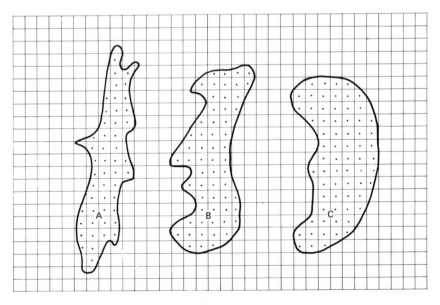

The diagrams given on page 135 show three imaginary islands which have been drawn on squared paper. We can compare their areas by counting squares.

By counting squares the approximate area of A is 49 squares. We include a square if more than half of it is within the area, but neglect it if more than half is outside. Similarly the area of B is 59 squares and the area of C is 68 squares. It follows that C has the largest area and A the smallest.

The value of any area may be found by counting squares, but it would simplify things considerably if we could build up areas from basic shapes, which we measured in acceptable units. The simplest area to consider is the square.

THE SQUARE

The area of a square of side 3 cm is $3 \times 3 \text{ cm}^2 = 9 \text{ cm}^2$, i.e. 9 squares, each of side 1 cm are required to cover completely a square of side 3 cm.

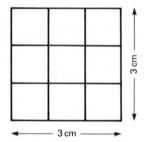

Similarly we can show that the area of a square of side x units is x^2 square units.

The perimeter of a square is the sum of the lengths of the four equal sides. Thus the perimeter (P) of a square of side x units is given by:

$$P = 4x \text{ units}$$

THE RECTANGLE

The number of squares of side 1 cm required to cover completely a rectangle which is 4 cm long and 3 cm wide is $4 \times 3 = 12$, i.e. the area of a rectangle measuring 4 cm by 3 cm is 12 cm^2.

Similarly, if a rectangle measures L units by B units, the number of unit squares required to cover it will be given by B rows, each row containing L squares, i.e. $L \times B$ squares.

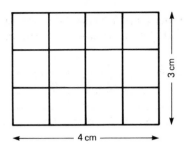

Thus the area (A) of a rectangle which is L units long and B units wide is given by:

$$A = L \times B \text{ square units}$$

The perimeter of this rectangle is the sum of the lengths of the four sides, two of length L units and two of length B units.

i.e. $\quad\quad\quad\quad$ Perimeter $(P) = 2L + 2B$ units

$$= 2(L + B) \text{ units}$$

EXAMPLE 1 $\quad$ Find (a) the perimeter, (b) the area of the given figure. All dimensions are in centimetres.

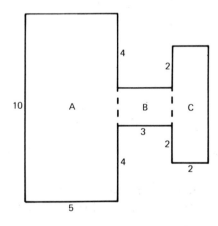

(a) Beginning at the top left hand corner of the diagram and moving clockwise, the perimeter of the figure is given by $P = 5 + 4 + 3 + 2 + 2 + 6 + 2 + 2 + 3 + 4 + 5 + 10 \text{ cm} = 48 \text{ cm}$.

(b) Dividing the given figure into three rectangles A, B and C:

$$\text{Area of A} = 10 \times 5 \text{ cm}^2 = 50 \text{ cm}^2$$

$$\text{Area of B} = 3 \times 2 \text{ cm}^2 = 6 \text{ cm}^2$$

$$\text{Area of C} = 6 \times 2 \text{ cm}^2 = 12 \text{ cm}^2$$

$$\therefore \quad \text{Total area of figure} = 68 \text{ cm}^2$$

EXAMPLE 2   The area of a rectangle, which is 9 m long, is 72 m^2.
Find (a) its breadth, (b) its perimeter.

(a) Since $A = L \times B$

$$72 = 9 \times B$$

i.e.
$$\text{Breadth} = \frac{72}{9} \text{ cm} = 8 \text{ cm}$$

$\therefore$ the rectangle is 8 cm in breadth.

(b) Perimeter $= 2(L + B)$ units

$$= 2(9 + 8) \text{ cm}$$

$$= 2 \times 17 \text{ cm}$$

i.e.   Perimeter $= 34$ cm

EXAMPLE 3   The floor of a hall measuring 30 m by 22 m is to be
covered with square floor tiles of side 50 cm. How
many tiles are required? If the tiles are sold only in
complete boxes containing 50 tiles, how much will it
cost to tile the floor at £8.46 per box?

Method 1

Laying one row of tiles against the long wall requires
$30 \text{ m} \div \frac{1}{2} \text{ m} = 60$ tiles,

and laying one row of tiles against the short wall
requires $22 \text{ m} \div \frac{1}{2} \text{ m} = 44$ tiles.

$\therefore$ Number of tiles required $= 60 \times 44 = 2640$.

Method 2

Area of floor to be covered $= 30 \times 22 \text{ m}^2$

Area of one tile $= \frac{1}{2} \times \frac{1}{2} \text{ m}^2$

$$\text{Number of tiles required} = \frac{\text{area of floor}}{\text{area of one tile}}$$

$$= \frac{30 \times 22 \text{ m}^2}{\frac{1}{2} \times \frac{1}{2} \text{ m}^2}$$

$$= 30 \times 22 \times 2 \times 2$$

$$= 2640$$

Method 3

Area of floor $= 3000 \times 2200 \text{ cm}^2$

Area of one tile $= 50 \times 50 \text{ cm}^2$

$$\text{Number of tiles required} \;=\; \frac{3000 \times 2200 \,\cancel{cm^2}}{50 \times 50 \,\cancel{cm^2}}$$

$$= 2640$$

$$\text{Number of boxes of tiles required} \;=\; \frac{2640}{50} = 52\tfrac{4}{5}$$

$\therefore$ 53 boxes must be purchased

Cost of 53 boxes at £8.46 per box $=$ £8.46 $\times$ 53

$$= \text{£448.38}$$

EXAMPLE 4

A rectangular vegetable garden measuring 18.5 m by 14 m is surrounded by a path of uniform width 1 m. Find (a) the area of the path, (b) the total perimeter of the path.

(a) If the path is 1 m wide the large rectangle measures 20.5 m by 16 m and therefore has an area of $20.5 \times 16 \text{ m}^2 = 328 \text{ m}^2$

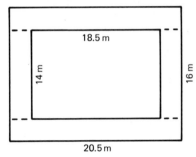

18.5 m

14 m

16 m

20.5 m

Area of small rectangle (the vegetable garden)

$$= 18.5 \times 14 \text{ m}^2 = 259 \text{ m}^2$$

$\therefore$ Area of path $= 328 - 259 \text{ m}^2$

$$= 69 \text{ m}^2$$

The area may also be found by dividing the path into four rectangles, as shown in the diagram.

Then Area of path $= (20.5 + 14 + 20.5 + 14) \text{ m}^2$

$$= 69 \text{ m}^2$$

(b) External perimeter of path $= 2(20.5 + 16) \text{ m}$

$$= 73 \text{ m}$$

Internal perimeter of path $= 2(18.5 + 14) \text{ m}$

$$= 65 \text{ m}$$

$\therefore$ Total perimeter $= (73 + 65) \text{ m} = 138 \text{ m}$

EXERCISE 52

By counting squares determine which is (a) the largest, (b) the smallest,
in each of the following:

1.

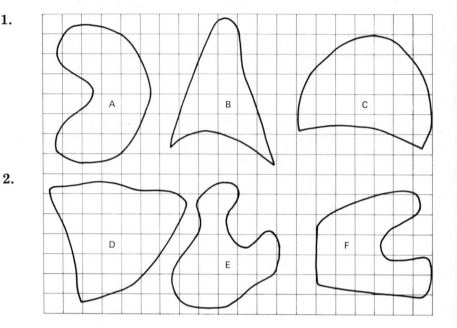

2.

Find (a) the perimeter, (b) the area, for each of the following figures
(all measurements are in centimetres):

3.

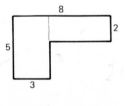

4.

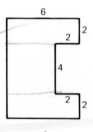

5.

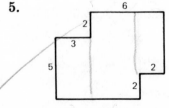

6.

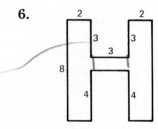

7.

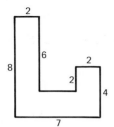

8.

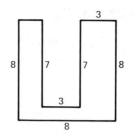

9.

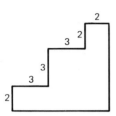

10.

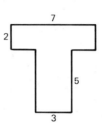

11.

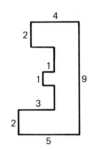

12.

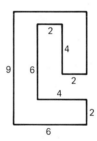

13.

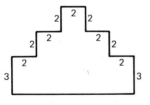

14.

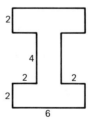

Find (a) the perimeter, (b) the area, for each of the squares whose sides are:

15. 2 cm   **16.** 3 km   **17.** 5 m   **18.** 7 mm

19. 0.5 cm   **20.** 0.75 km   **21.** 1.2 cm   **22.** 0.4 km.

Find (a) the perimeter, (b) the area, of rectangles measuring:

23. 4 cm by 3 cm   **24.** 12 mm by 8 mm

25. 7 m by 5 m   **26.** 10 m by 80 m.

Find the area of each of the following rectangles, giving your answer in the units given in brackets.

	LENGTH	BREADTH	
27.	5 cm	5 mm	(mm^2)
28.	1 m	40 cm	(cm^2)
29.	26 m	5 m	(m^2)
30.	1.5 km	750 m	(km^2)
31.	360 m	450 m	(hectares)

32. Fill in the blanks in the following table which gives data for various rectangles:

	LENGTH	BREADTH	AREA	PERIMETER
(a)	5 cm		20 cm^2	
(b)		10 m		50 m
(c)	3.4 cm		8.84 cm^2	
(d)	18 mm			60 mm
(e)	1.5 m		1.125 m^2	

33. A lounge measuring 3.5 m by 3 m is to be covered with square carpet tiles each of side 50 cm. How many tiles are required?

34. How many rectangular tiles measuring 16 cm by 8 cm are required to tile a wall 2 m long and 2.88 m high? If they are sold only in complete boxes containing 25 tiles, at £9.50 a box, find the cost of this tiling.

35. A rectangular building plot is 30 m long and 8.5 m wide. Find:
    (a) the perimeter of the plot
    (b) its area in m^2.

36. John Price has a greenhouse which measures 9.5 m by 3.5 m, and wishes to use it for plants each of which will require an area of 2500 cm^2. How many plants should he buy?

37. Find the length of the side of a square which has an area equal to the area of a rectangle measuring (a) 9 m by 4 m, (b) 24 cm by 60 mm, (c) 45 cm by 20 cm.

38. Peter Evans buys 86 square paving stones, each of side 50 cm, with a view to paving his yard which is rectangular and measures 6.5 m by 3.5 m. What area is unpaved when he has laid all his paving stones? How many more are required to complete the job?

39. The diagram shows a flag, all dimensions being in centimetres. Find (a) the unshaded area, (b) the shaded area.

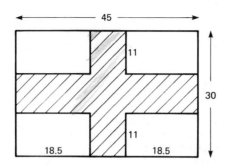

40. Greengrass fertiliser costs £14.20 for a 10 kg bag. If it is to be used at the rate of 30 g per square metre, find:
    (a) the cost of fertilising a rectangular lawn measuring 15.5 m by 12 m
    (b) the quantity of fertiliser remaining.

41. A rectangular lawn measuring 12 m by 10.5 m is to be bordered on two adjacent sides by a path 0.75 m wide. Find the area of this path.

42. An open-air rectangular swimming pool measuring 20 m by 15 m is surrounded by a path 1 m wide. If the path is made of square paving stones of side 50 cm, how many stones are required?

43. A rectangular table top is 1.5 m long and 80 cm wide. A rectangular cloth is to be made which will cover the table and have an over-hang of 10 cm. Find:
    (a) the area of the table cloth in square metres
    (b) the area of the overhang in square metres.

44. A rectangular carpet is laid in a rectangular room measuring 4.2 m by 3.6 m so that there is a uniform uncarpeted border 60 cm wide surrounding the carpet. Calculate:
    (a) the perimeter of the carpet
    (b) the area which is uncarpeted.

45. The page of a dictionary measures 24 cm by 17 cm with the text set out in two columns separated by a 5 mm margin. At the edge of the page is a border which is 1.5 cm wide except at the bottom of the page where it is only 1 cm wide. Find the total area of text if the dictionary has 1640 similar pages.

THE PARALLELOGRAM

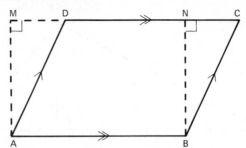

ABCD is a parallelogram with AB parallel to DC and AD parallel to BC. BN is the perpendicular from B to CD, and AM is the perpendicular from A to CD produced. Simple geometry tells us that the area of triangle AMD is equal to the area of triangle BNC. It follows that the area of the parallelogram ABCD is equal to the area of the rectangle ABNM.

Since   Area of the rectangle $= AB \times BN$

then   Area of the parallelogram ABCD $= AB \times BN$

i.e.   Area of parallelogram $=$ base $\times$ height

THE TRIANGLE

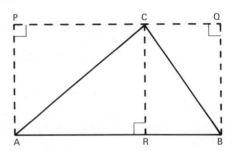

If AP and BQ are the perpendiculars from A and B in triangle ABC to the line through C parallel to AB, and R is the foot of the perpendicular from C to AB, then ABQP is a rectangle with area $AB \times BQ$. But $BQ = CR$. Therefore area of rectangle $= AB \times CR$, where CR is the perpendicular height of the triangle.

simple geometry gives:

$$\triangle CBQ = \triangle CBR \quad \text{and} \quad \triangle CPA = \triangle CRA$$

i.e. the area of the triangle ABC is half the area of the rectangle ABQP.

$\therefore$ Area of triangle ABC $= \frac{1}{2} AB \times CR$

More generally:

            Area of a triangle $= \frac{1}{2}$ base $\times$ perpendicular height

THE TRAPEZIUM

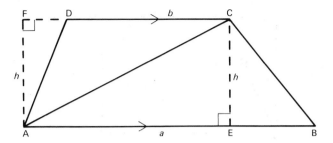

The diagonal AC divides the trapezium into two triangles.

$$\text{Area } \triangle ABC = \tfrac{1}{2} AB \times CE = \tfrac{1}{2} ah$$

and
$$\triangle ADC = \tfrac{1}{2} DC \times AF = \tfrac{1}{2} bh$$

∴
$$\text{Area of trapezium} = \tfrac{1}{2} ah + \tfrac{1}{2} bh$$

$$= \left(\frac{a+b}{2} \right) h$$

i.e.   Half the sum of the parallel sides × the perpendicular distance between them

EXERCISE 53

Questions 1 to 6 refer to the following diagram:

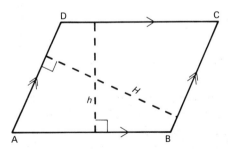

ABCD is a parallelogram with h the distance between AB and DC, and H the distance between BC and AD.

1. If $AB = 12$ cm, $AD = 8$ cm and $h = 6.5$ cm, find (a) the area of the parallelogram, (b) the value of H.

2. If $AB = 8$ cm, $h = 7$ cm and $H = 5$ cm, find (a) the area of the parallelogram, (b) the length of AD.

3. If $DC = 14$ cm, $AD = 10$ cm and $H = 10\tfrac{1}{2}$ cm, find (a) the area of the parallelogram, (b) the value of h.

4. If the area of the parallelogram is $48\,\text{cm}^2$, and $H = 2h = 8\,\text{cm}$, find the lengths of AB and BC.

5. If the area of the parallelogram is $72\,\text{cm}^2$, $AB = 18\,\text{cm}$ and $AD = 12\,\text{cm}$, find h and H.

6. If the area of the parallelogram is $108\,\text{cm}^2$, $h = 9\,\text{cm}$ and $3AB = 4AD$, find (a) AB, (b) AD, (c) H.

Questions 7 to 13 refer to the following diagram:

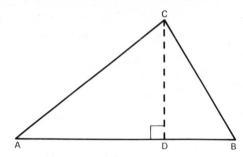

Find the area of triangle ABC if:

7. $AB = 12\,\text{cm}$, $CD = 8\,\text{cm}$

8. $AB = 20\,\text{cm}$, $CD = 13\,\text{cm}$

9. $AB = 8.4\,\text{cm}$, $CD = 5.2\,\text{cm}$

10. $AB = 2.25\,\text{cm}$, $CD = 5\frac{1}{3}\,\text{cm}$.

11. Find CD if the area of the triangle is $48\,\text{cm}^2$ and $AB = 12\,\text{cm}$.

12. Find AB if the area of the triangle is $13.65\,\text{cm}^2$ and $CD = 4.2\,\text{cm}$.

13. Find CD if the area of the triangle is $14.04\,\text{cm}^2$ and $AB = 5.2\,\text{cm}$.

Questions 14 to 19 refer to the following diagram:

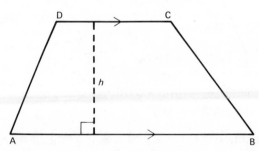

Find the area of trapezium ABCD if:

14. $AB = 12\,\text{cm}$, $DC = 8\,\text{cm}$ and $h = 8\,\text{cm}$.

15. $AB = 18.7\,\text{cm}$, $DC = 11.3\,\text{cm}$ and $h = 5.5\,\text{cm}$.

16. $AB = 7.7\,\text{cm}$, $DC = 4.3\,\text{cm}$ and $h = 3.7\,\text{cm}$.

17. Find h if the area of the trapezium is $77\,\text{cm}^2$ and the parallel sides have lengths $14\,\text{cm}$ and $8\,\text{cm}$.

18. Find AB if the area of the trapezium is $200\,\text{cm}^2$, $DC = 24\,\text{cm}$ and $h = 10\,\text{cm}$.

19. Find the lengths of the parallel sides AB and CD, given that the area of the trapezium is $60\,\text{cm}^2$, the distance between the parallel sides is $6\,\text{cm}$ and $2AB = 3CD$.

20. Find the distance between the parallel sides of a trapezium with area $117.3\,\text{cm}^2$ if the parallel sides are respectively of length $15.4\,\text{cm}$ and $12.2\,\text{cm}$.

VOLUME

The volume of a solid is the amount of space it occupies. The volume of an irregular solid may be found by measuring the amount of water displaced from a full container when the solid is totally submerged in the water. We measure volume in cubic units, thus $1\,\text{m}^3$ is the volume occupied by a cube of side one metre. The units chosen vary according to what is being measured and what is considered most suitable. Thus the volume of a small object such as a half-penny may be measured in cubic millimetres (mm^3), the volume of a typical book in cubic centimetres (cm^3) and the volume of a room in cubic metres (m^3).

The simplest solid to give a general expression for its volume is the rectangular block or cuboid. The volume of a wooden block measuring $4\,\text{cm}$ by $3\,\text{cm}$ by $2\,\text{cm}$ would be $24\,\text{cm}^3$, because 12 cubes of side $1\,\text{cm}$ would be required to cover the area on which the block stands, together with another 12 blocks to bring the height or thickness up to $2\,\text{cm}$.

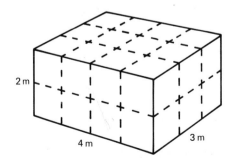

i.e. Volume of block $(V) = 4 \times 3 \times 2\,\text{cm}^3$

i.e. $V = 24\,\text{cm}^3$

It is only a short step to generalise this result so that we can say that the volume (V) of a cuboid L units long, B units wide and H units in height is given by:

$$V = L \times B \times H \text{ cubic units}$$

Care must be taken to check that all dimensions are given in the same units.

The metric units of volume in common use are related as follows:

$$1 \, cm^3 = 10^3 \, mm^3 = 1000 \, mm^3$$
$$1 \, m^3 = 100^3 \, cm^3 = 1\,000\,000 \, cm^3$$

The internal volume of a container, such as a milk bottle or a water tank is called its *capacity*, i.e. the capacity of a container is the volume inside it. We usually measure capacity in litres, where:

$$1 \, litre = 1000 \, cm^3$$
$$\therefore \quad 1000 \, litres = 1 \, m^3$$

When the capacity is small, the millilitre (ml) is used; e.g. a 5 ml spoon is often used for measuring medicines.

$$1000 \, ml = 1 \, litre$$
$$\therefore \quad 1 \, ml = 1 \, cm^3$$

EXAMPLE 5

Find the volume of a concrete block measuring 30 cm by 20 cm by 10 cm, giving your answer in (a) cubic centimetres, (b) cubic metres.

(a) Volume $= L \times B \times H$

$$= 30 \times 20 \times 10 \, cm^3$$

$$= 6000 \, cm^3$$

(b) If we work in metres

Volume $= 0.3 \times 0.2 \times 0.1 \, m^3$

$$= 0.006 \, m^3$$

This result may also be obtained by dividing the result for (a) by 100^3.

EXAMPLE 6

An open mould for making concrete blocks is shown in the diagram on page 149. The external dimensions of the mould, which is everywhere 3 cm thick, are 42 cm by 24 cm by 12 cm. Calculate (a) the volume of a concrete block, (b) the volume of material used in making the mould.

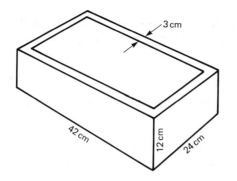

(a) The internal dimensions of the mould will be:

Length: $(42-6) = 36$ cm

Breadth: $(24-6) = 18$ cm

Depth: $(12-3) = 9$ cm

∴   Volume of a concrete block

$$= 36 \times 18 \times 9 \, \text{cm}^3$$

$$= 5832 \, \text{cm}^3$$

(b) Volume of the external cuboid

$$= 42 \times 24 \times 12 \, \text{cm}^3$$

$$= 12\,096 \, \text{cm}^3$$

∴ Amount of material used in making the block

$$= (12\,096 - 5832) \, \text{cm}^3$$

$$= 6264 \, \text{cm}^3$$

EXAMPLE 7   The diagram on page 150 shows the cross-section of a girder 4.5 m long, all dimensions on the diagram being in centimetres. Find:

(a) the area of cross-section in square centimetres,

(b) the volume of the girder in (i) cubic centimetres, (ii) cubic metres,

(c) the mass of the girder if $1 \, \text{cm}^3$ of the metal used has a mass of 7.8 g. Give your answer correct to the nearest kilogram.

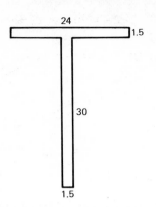

(a) Consider the area of cross-section as two rectangles:

Area of cross-section $= (24 \times 1.5 + 30 \times 1.5)\,\text{cm}^2$

$= (36 + 45)\,\text{cm}^2$

$= 81\,\text{cm}^2$

(b) Volume of girder $=$ area of cross-section
$\times$ length

$= 81 \times 450\,\text{cm}^3$

$= 36\,450\,\text{cm}^3$

Since $100^3\,\text{cm}^3 = 1\,\text{m}^3$:

$$\text{Volume of girder} = \frac{36\,450}{100 \times 100 \times 100}\,\text{m}^3$$

$= 0.036\,45\,\text{m}^3$

(c) Mass of girder $=$ volume in $\text{cm}^3 \times 7.8\,\text{g}$

$= 36\,450 \times 7.8\,\text{g}$

$= 284\,310\,\text{g}$

$= 284.31\,\text{kg}$

$= 284\,\text{kg}$ correct to the nearest kilogram

EXERCISE 54

1. Find the volume of a cube with side:
   (a) $8\,\text{cm}$ (b) $4\,\text{mm}$ (c) $5\,\text{m}$ (d) $2.3\,\text{cm}$
   (e) $0.6\,\text{km}$ (f) $\frac{3}{5}\,\text{m}$.

Use the data below to find the volumes of the following rectangular solids:

	LENGTH	BREADTH	HEIGHT
2.	5 cm	4 cm	3 cm
3.	12 m	8 m	7 m
4.	10 cm	4.3 cm	3.5 cm
5.	5 km	2.4 km	1.5 km
6.	1.5 km	0.75 km	0.5 km

7. Find the side of a cube if its volume is:

   (a) $216 \, \text{mm}^3$ (b) $0.125 \, \text{m}^3$ (c) $\dfrac{8}{27} \, \text{cm}^3$.

Find the missing quantity for rectangular solids with the data below:

	LENGTH	BREADTH	HEIGHT	VOLUME
8.	12 cm	8 cm		$576 \, \text{cm}^3$
9.		9 mm	8 mm	$792 \, \text{mm}^3$
10.	1 m	23 cm		$18\,400 \, \text{cm}^3$
11.		1.4 mm	0.5 mm	$3.5 \, \text{mm}^3$
12.	2.5 cm		0.6 cm	$1.2 \, \text{cm}^3$
13.	1.5 m		0.5 m	$\frac{9}{16} \, \text{m}^3$

14. Find the volume of a rectangular room measuring 10 m by 6 m by 3 m. If $4.5 \, \text{m}^3$ of airspace is required for each person, what is the maximum number of people who may use the room at the same time?

15. A classroom measuring 8 m by 6 m is to be used for a form of 32 pupils. If $5 \, \text{m}^3$ of airspace is allowed for each pupil, how high should the ceiling be?

16. How many litres of water can be stored in a rectangular tank measuring 1.2 m by 80 cm by 50 cm?

17. Find the cost of a rectangular piece of timber measuring 20 cm by 8 cm which is 4 m long, if the price of the timber is £55 per cubic metre.

18. Find the mass of a metal bar measuring 3 m by 8 cm by 4 cm if $1 \, \text{cm}^3$ of the metal has a mass of 9.4 g. Give your answer (a) in grams, (b) in kilograms.

19. How many rectangular packets of tea measuring 12 cm by 4 cm by 4 cm may be packed in a cardboard box measuring 48 cm by 24 cm by 16 cm?

20. If the total surface area of a cube is $150 \, \text{cm}^2$, find its volume.

21. A rectangular tank measuring 1.3 m by 80 cm by 80 cm is full of water. If 400 litres of water is drawn off into another tank 1 m long and 80 cm wide, find the depth of water in each tank.

22. The page of a book measuring 20 cm by 12 cm is 0.05 mm thick. Find the volume of a page in cubic centimetres. Hence find the volume of the book if it has 220 pages.

23. A rectangular block of lead measuring 15 cm by 9 cm by 6 cm is melted down and recast, without any loss of volume, into cubes of side 3 cm. How many cubes are produced?

24. The external dimensions of a closed rectangular box are 12 cm by 10 cm by 9 cm. If the wood is everywhere 5 mm thick, find:
(a) the volume of the interior of the box
(b) the volume of wood used in its construction.

25. An open rectangular tank has internal dimensions 1.2 m by 75 cm by 60 cm. If the metal is everywhere 2.5 mm thick, find:
(a) the number of litres of water which the tank will hold
(b) the volume of metal used in its construction.

26. The diagram shows the cross-section of a girder which is 4 m long. All measurements are in centimetres. Find the volume of the girder in (a) cubic centimetres, (b) cubic metres.

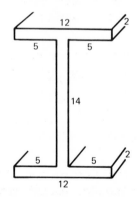

27. The diagram shows the cross-section of a hollow metal girder 6 m long which is everywhere 7.5 mm thick. Find the volume of metal in the girder in (a) cubic centimetres, (b) cubic metres.

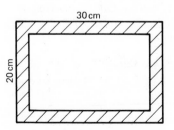

28. The diagram shows the cross-section of a girder 5.5 m long. All dimensions are in centimetres. Calculate:
    (a) the volume of the girder in cubic centimetres
    (b) the mass of the girder in kilograms if $1\,cm^3$ of the girder has a mass of 8 g.

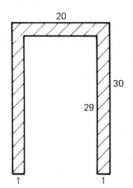

29. A 10 litre can of washing-up liquid has a rectangular cross-section measuring 25 cm by 10 cm. How tall is the can?

30. How many concrete blocks measuring 50 cm by 25 cm by 12.5 cm may be cast from $1\,m^3$ of concrete?

31. A 3 m length of timber has a uniform cross-section in the form of a rhombus of area $4.5\,cm^2$. Find its volume in cubic centimetres.

32. The area of cross-section of a 16 cm bar of chocolate is in the form of an equilateral triangle of area $4.5\,cm^2$. Find the volume of chocolate in the bar.

33. The diagram shows the cross-section of a horse trough which is everywhere a trapezium, the parallel sides of which have lengths 30 cm and 24 cm. If the trough is 30 cm deep and 2.5 m long, find the volume of water it will hold when full, giving your answer in cubic metres correct to three significant figures.

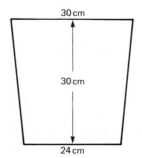

34. The diagram shows the cross-section of a water channel which is 10 m long. How many litres of water will it hold when full?

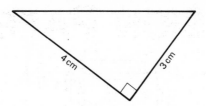

35. The diagram shows the cross-section of a uniform metal bar which is 3.5 m long. Find:
    (a) its cross-sectional area in square centimetres
    (b) its volume in cubic centimetres correct to three significant figures
    (c) its mass, correct to the nearest kilogram, if $1 \, cm^3$ of the metal has a mass of 8.2 g.

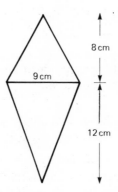

REVISION PAPERS
26-50

PAPER 26

1. How many bars of chocolate costing 45 p each may be bought for £10 and how much change is there?

2. A car uses 22 litres of petrol for a journey of 594 km. How many litres are required for a journey of 351 km?

3. Divide £8.55 between Anne and David in the ratio 7 : 12.

4. An article is bought for £1.80. Find its selling price if it is sold (a) at a gain of 10%, (b) at a loss of 10%.

5. George Waters earns £800 per month. He receives a rise of 12%, but income tax is deducted from his gross pay at 18%, together with a further deduction of 14% of gross pay for national insurance and pension contribution. Calculate his net monthly pay after he has received his rise.

PAPER 27

1. (a) Express $\dfrac{13}{20}$ and $\dfrac{7}{4}$ as percentages.

    (b) Express 45% and 320% as fractions in their lowest terms.

2. A factory worker is paid £2.76 per hour for a $37\frac{1}{2}$ hour week. If deductions for national insurance and income tax amount to £18.56, calculate her 'take-home' pay.

3. Simplify $\left(\dfrac{3}{7}\times\dfrac{5}{9}\right)\div\left(6\dfrac{1}{4}-5\dfrac{4}{15}\right)$.

155

4. A lounge measures 4.5 m by 3.5 m and has a ceiling 2.6 m high. Calculate the number of rolls of wallpaper, each 10 m long and 52 cm wide, required to paper the walls of this room. Allow 7.5 m² for doors and windows and add 10% to allow for matching the pattern.

5. A school hall measures 21 m by 12 m. How many square tiles of side 25 cm are required to cover the floor? If they can only be bought in complete boxes containing 25 tiles, how many boxes are required?

PAPER 28

1. Divide £35.84 between George, Harold and Idris in the ratio 5:4:7.

2. Find (a) $10 - 7.364 + 0.243 + 1.64$, (b) $0.0492 \div 0.123$.

3. What number when increased by 15% becomes 207?

4. An auctioneer arranges the transfer of a piece of furniture from Mr Martin's house to the saleroom at a cost of £26.50. At auction the piece is sold for £755. If the auctioneer's commission is 12% of the selling price, how much could Mr Martin expect to receive from the sale?

5. If 46 rolls of cloth each 100 m in length may be bought for £8464, how many 50 m rolls of a similar quality cloth may be bought for £6808?

PAPER 29

1. Simplify $\dfrac{1\frac{3}{8} + 1\frac{5}{7}}{2\frac{6}{7} + 1\frac{3}{4}}$.

2. The representative fraction of a map is 1:50 000. Calculate the distance in kilometres between two points which are 5.4 cm apart on the map.

3. Simplify (a) $\dfrac{(-12)\times 3\times(-8)}{4\times(-16)}$, (b) $\dfrac{(-4)^2\times(-3)\times(-6)}{-36}$.

4. A sum of money was divided between four girls. The first received $\frac{1}{3}$ of it, the second $\frac{2}{5}$, the third $\frac{1}{6}$ and the fourth £1.86. Calculate (a) the sum of money, (b) the amount received by the first girl.

5. A house cost £23 000 to build on a site costing £5600. What weekly rent must the owner charge to have a return of 10% on his investment after paying $\frac{1}{3}$ of the rent for rates and repairs?

PAPER 30

1. Find $\frac{4}{7}$ of £164.29.

2. A drum contains 36 litres of oil. If $8\frac{1}{3}\%$ leaks out, how much remains?

3. Evaluate $51.6 \div 2.45$ giving your answer correct to (a) the nearest whole number, (b) three significant figures, (c) two decimal places.

4. A shopkeeper allows a discount of $2\frac{1}{2}\%$ for cash. Find the cash price of an article marked £244.

5. During a school charity week £2475 was collected. If the proceeds were divided between five charities A, B, C, D and E in the ratio $3:4:5:6:7$. how much more would charity E receive than charity A?

PAPER 31

1. What percentage is (a) 294 of 840, (b) 150 g of 2 kg, (c) 655 m of 2 km?

2. Simplify $\left(2\dfrac{1}{8} - \dfrac{1}{5}\right) \div \left(1\dfrac{1}{10} + 2\dfrac{4}{5}\right)$.

3. A grocer bought 850 cans of tomatoes at 21 p each and sold them at $23\frac{1}{2}$ p. Find the profit.

4. An oil-fired boiler consumes 15 litres of oil a day. If the tank which supplies the boiler with oil contains sufficient oil to last 21 days, how many days would the oil supply last if cold weather caused the consumption to rise to 18 litres per day?

5. A photograph measuring 24 cm by 18 cm is mounted on a rectangular piece of card so that it has a 3.5 cm border all round. Calculate the area of card visible.

PAPER 32

1. (a) Multiply £3.49 by 27. (b) Divide £50.35 by 19.

2. Ken is 21 years old, Len 23 and Morgan 18. Divide £21 700 between them in the ratio of their ages.

3. If the coach fare for an 86 mile journey is £6.45, what is the coach fare for a journey of 125 miles? How far could you travel for £5?

4. A square has a side of length 8 cm. Find the percentage change in area if:
   (a) the length of each side is increased by 25%
   (b) the length of each side is decreased by 25%.

5. A dealer buys a number of tins of paint for £206.58. By selling them at £4.20 each he makes a profit of £70.62. How many tins did he buy?

PAPER 33

1. Simplify $\left(2\dfrac{1}{3} + 3\dfrac{1}{4}\right) \div \left(1\dfrac{1}{4} + 5\dfrac{5}{12}\right).$

2. In a sale five articles may be bought for the price of four. What percentage reduction is this?

3. A man saved £750 in a year. The next year his savings were 10% greater than the first year, and the following year his savings were 5% greater than his savings the second year. How much did he save during the three years?

4. In a certain factory 116 workers are required to produce 6612 articles in a week. How many workers would be required to produce 7638 articles in a week, assuming that they all work at the same rate?

5. The diagram shows an L-shaped lounge. How many floor tiles, each measuring 25 cm by 25 cm, are required to tile the floor? If they are sold only in complete boxes, 12 to a box, how many boxes must be purchased and how many tiles are left over?

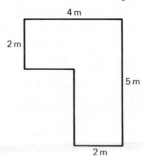

PAPER 34

1. Find the HCF of 4284 and 5355. What is the smallest number by which 4284 must be multiplied to make it a perfect square?

2. Write down the next two numbers in the sequence 3, 22, 59, 120, ...

3. Working in the binary system only, find (a) $1101101+11110$, (b) $10000-1010$, (c) 1011×111, (d) $1001000\div1100$.

4. If £10.54 is divided into equal numbers of 2 p, 10 p and 50 p coins, how many of each are there?

5. A lawn measuring 42 m by 25 m requires fertiliser at the rate of 56 g per square metre. How many 10 kg bags of fertiliser must be purchased?

PAPER 35

1. Simplify (a) $(-16)\times(-2)\times(-3)^2$, (b) $[60\div(-12)]\times(-5)$.

2. What must be added to $\left(\dfrac{2}{3}-\dfrac{4}{7}\right)\div\dfrac{1}{2}$ to make it equal to $\dfrac{1}{2}\div\left(\dfrac{2}{3}-\dfrac{4}{7}\right)$?

3. Divide 23.474 by 0.97 and multiply your result by 17.5.

4. If it takes 24 men 18 days to paint a bridge, how long would it take 9 men to paint the same bridge, assuming that they all work at the same rate?

5. A retailer bought 45 garden seats for £5058. How much should each be sold for to make a profit of 35%?

PAPER 36

1. Simplify $2\dfrac{3}{4}$ of $5\dfrac{1}{8}\div\left(2\dfrac{3}{4}+5\dfrac{1}{2}\right)$.

2. Find the percentage increase if 155 is increased to 186.

3. How many glasses, each of which will hold 50 ml, may be filled to $\frac{2}{3}$ full from a 1 litre bottle?

4. If a train journey of 216 km costs £10.80, find the fare for a journey of 376 km. How far could I expect to travel for £10?

5. Find the cost of:

   12 kg of potatoes at 36 p per kg
   34 plants at 17 p each
   3 lengths of fencing at £12.49 per length
   8 bags of fertiliser at £14.28 each.

PAPER 37

1. (a) Express 440 g as a decimal of 2.75 kg.

    (b) Express $\frac{7}{45}$ as a decimal correct to two decimal places.

2. A sum of money is divided between three girls. Wendy receives $\frac{1}{9}$ of it, Tracey three times as much as Wendy, and Susan receives £4.95. How much does Tracey receive?

3. A bucket of water when full has a mass of 16.5 kg. If its mass when half-full is 9 kg, calculate the mass of the bucket.

4. An oak beam is 12 m long, 10 cm wide and 15 cm deep. If 1 m³ of oak has a mass of 800 kg, calculate the mass of the beam.

5. Seats in a cinema were sold at £3, £2.50 and £2. If the numbers of people who bought seats at these prices were in the ratio 3:4:5, find the size of the audience if the total receipts amounted to £1914. How many bought the cheapest seats?

PAPER 38

1. Simplify (a) $9 \times (-2)^2 \div (-8)$, (b) $(-24) \div [(-3) \times 4]$.

2. (a) Express (i) 743 as a binary number, (ii) 1 1 0 0 1 1 1 as a denary number.

    (b) Find (i) $23_5 + 24_5$, (ii) $232_5 - 34_5$.

3. A carpet measuring 4 m by 3.5 m costs £210. How much will a similar carpet cost which measures 4.5 m by 5 m?

4. A company agrees to take on 37 new workers if the existing workforce agree to a reduction in the working week from 42 to 40 hours. By doing this the company saves £428 if the hourly rate is £2. How many were employed at the factory before the extra staff were taken on?

5. A shipping company advertise a 15 day 4286 mile cruise at £1500. Calculate the cost per mile correct to the nearest penny. Is this cheaper or dearer per mile than the local bus service where a particular $1\frac{4}{5}$ mile journey costs 70 p?

PAPER 39

1. Find $1\frac{5}{7}$ of $\frac{1}{2} \div 3\frac{3}{7}$.

2. What is the cost of 96 boxes of soap at £1.46 each?

3. Of what sum of money is £4.93 equal to $14\frac{1}{2}$%?

4. A comprehensive school is on two sites. In the lower school, which is on one site, there are 240 boys, and in the middle and upper schools, which are on a separate site, there are 477 boys. If boys form 48% of lower school but 53% of middle and upper school, how many girls are there in the whole school? What percentage of the whole school are girls?

5. An open rectangular box with external dimensions 10 cm by 8 cm by 6 cm is made from wood 5 mm thick. Calculate (a) its capacity, (b) the volume of wood used to make it.

PAPER 40

1. Simplify (a) 0.043×3.72, (b) $2.394 \div 0.456$.

2. (a) Change 24_5, 42_6 and 32_4 into denary numbers.
   (b) Calculate (i) 10101×1101, (ii) $101010 \div 110$.

3. A hot water tank is $\frac{5}{8}$ full. If 36.5 litres is drawn off for a bath, it is $\frac{19}{45}$ full. How many litres does the tank hold when full?

4. David Peters left $\frac{2}{5}$ of his assets to his wife, $\frac{1}{3}$ to his son, with the remainder to be divided equally between eight charities. If each charity received £2564, how much did his wife get?

5. For a concert 500 seats are on sale at £12, 260 at £9 and 488 at £7.50. If the most expensive seats are $\frac{3}{4}$ taken, the £9 seats $\frac{12}{13}$ taken and the cheapest seats $\frac{7}{8}$ taken, find the total takings for the concert. How much more would they have taken had all the seats been sold?

PAPER 41

1. Simplify $\left(1\frac{3}{5} + 2\frac{2}{3}\right) \div \left(6\frac{19}{24} - 1\frac{1}{4}\right)$.

2. How long would a boy take to walk 2.5 km to school if he takes seventy 85 cm paces each minute? Give your answer correct to the nearest minute.

3. When $8\frac{1}{2}$% of the pupils in a school are absent, 1098 pupils are present. How many pupils are there in the school?

4. Find the cost of 23 m^2 of carpeting at £11.86 per square metre.

5. A greenhouse stands on an area measuring 12 m by 6 m. It is to be used for growing tomato plants, each plant requiring $\frac{2}{3}$ m². How many plants will the greenhouse take?

PAPER 42

1. Divide the sum of $2\frac{1}{2}$ and $3\frac{2}{5}$ by the difference between $5\frac{2}{3}$ and $4\frac{1}{6}$.

2. What is the least length of planking 15 cm wide which will be required to cover a floor 5 m long and 3 m wide?

3. Express:
   (a) 450 cm³ as a percentage of 2.5 litres
   (b) $\frac{2730}{4368}$ as a fraction in its lowest terms.

4. Twelve sets of the same stamps cost £13.20. There are four stamps in each set, the values of three of them being $\frac{2}{3}$, $\frac{5}{9}$ and $\frac{5}{6}$ of the value of the most expensive stamp. Find the value of each stamp in one set.

5. A wine merchant bought a 50 litre cask of sherry for £127.70. Some leaked out, but he sold what remained at £3.56 per litre thereby making a profit of £41.40. How many litres leaked out?

PAPER 43

1. Simplify $\dfrac{12\frac{1}{6} + 5\frac{1}{4}}{8\frac{3}{4} - 3\frac{1}{2}}$.

2. Of what mass in kilograms is 234 g equal to $9\frac{3}{4}$%?

3. Find the cost of wallpaper per square metre if a roll 10 m long and 52 cm wide costs £7.54.

4. Find the total area, in square metres, of sheet metal used to make an open rectangular water tank 1.5 m long, 1.1 m wide and 90 cm high. What volume of water, in cubic metres, does this hold? Find the mass of this water in kilograms if 1 m³ of water has a mass of 1 t.

5. To send a message costs 5 p a word plus an initial charge of 30 p. How much will it cost to send a message with 12 words? How many words are there in a message costing £1.10?

PAPER 44

1. My father was born in December 1952. How old was he in June 1983?

2. Divide the product of $2\frac{2}{3}$ and $1\frac{7}{8}$ by the difference between $5\frac{3}{7}$ and $3\frac{4}{5}$.

3. A passenger liner steaming at 22 knots takes 14 days to travel between two ports. By how much must it increase its speed to cut 3 days off the voyage?

4. Find the cost of 4.75 t of coal at £136 per tonne.

5. A given mass of sheet copper is sufficient to cover an area measuring 5 m by 4 m when it is 5 mm thick. What area could be covered with the same mass of copper using a sheet 3 mm thick?

PAPER 45

1. Arrange in descending order: $\dfrac{9}{16}, \dfrac{5}{8}, \dfrac{11}{20}, \dfrac{16}{30}$.

2. When the price of petrol was £1.86 per gallon a motorist's monthly petrol bill was £52.08. What was the increase in his monthly bill when petrol rose to £2.05 per gallon?

3. A guitar is marked at a price which gives the seller a profit of 45%, but a discount of 10% is given for cash. Find the net percentage profit. Find the cost price of such a guitar which, with discount, sells at £143.55.

4. George Foster is paid £2.54 per hour for a $38\frac{1}{2}$ hour week. Find his gross wage.

5. The external dimensions of a closed wooden rectangular box are 18 cm × 12 cm × 8 cm. If the wood is everywhere 4 mm thick, find:
   (a) the volume of space within the box
   (b) the volume of wood used to make the box.

PAPER 46

1. Simplify $\dfrac{2\frac{1}{4} - \frac{2}{3} \times 1\frac{5}{6}}{\frac{1}{5} \times 3\frac{1}{3} + \frac{13}{36}}$.

2. The smaller of two numbers is 14.6 and their sum is 38.4. Find their product.

3. Five men on a trek across the desert have sufficient water for 15 days. How long would the water last three of them?

4. A car does 38 miles per gallon on a 306 mile trip. How many complete gallons must be purchased for the journey? Find the cost of this petrol at £2.14 per gallon.

5. By selling a chair for £110.40 a shopkeeper loses 8%. What percentage must he gain on a similar chair to give him a gain of 10% on the two?

PAPER 47

1. If eight articles cost £27.68, find the cost of five.

2. Divide £784 between four brothers in the ratio $2:3:4:5$.

3. In a sale a shopkeeper reduced the price of everything in the shop by 15 p in the £. What was the original price of an article which has a sale price of £53.04?

4. Find the cost per square metre, correct to the nearest pound, of an Indian carpet measuring 4 m 20 cm by 3 m 45 cm, which sells for £1565.

5. The total mass of three parcels is 8.1 kg. If one of these parcels is 1.2 kg heavier than each of the other two, find the masses of the three parcels.

PAPER 48

1. Simplify $\dfrac{1\frac{1}{4} + 2\frac{11}{12}}{4\frac{1}{3} - 3\frac{1}{6}} \times 2\frac{1}{4} \div 3\frac{1}{8}$.

2. Convert the following into denary numbers:
   (a) 1210_3 (b) 1231_4 (c) 2054_8.

3. The population of Oakdale is 2970. Last year the population increased by 8%, and the previous year it increased by 10%. What was its population 2 years ago?

4. A boy is 16 years old now while his father is 44. Calculate the ratio of their ages (a) now, (b) 4 years ago, (c) in 12 years' time.

5. A second hand car dealer buys two similar cars for £1500 each. He sells the first at a loss of 6%. What percentage profit must he make on the second car in order to make a profit of 8% on the two?

Revision Papers

PAPER 49

1. If $\dfrac{1}{3}+\dfrac{1}{4}+\dfrac{1}{5}$ of a sum of money is £22.09, find $\dfrac{23}{47}$ of it.

2. What length of paper 52 cm wide is required to paper the walls of a room 4 m 14 cm long, 3 m, 14 cm wide and 2 m 80 cm in height? If each roll is 10 m long, how many rolls must be bought? What will they cost at £4.56 per roll?

3. If a machine can fill and seal 225 tins with beans in 3 minutes, how many tins could be filled and sealed in half an hour?

4. In a year Peter Eschle spends 63% of his income on household expenses, 18% on his car, 12% on incidental expenses, and saves the remainder. If he saves £987, calculate his annual income.

5. A closed rectangular box measures 12 cm by 8 cm by 6 cm and is made from wood 5 mm thick. Find the volume of wood used in cubic centimetres. If a second box which is twice as long, twice as wide and twice as high is to be made from wood of the same thickness, calculate the volume of wood required for this second box, in cubic centimetres.

PAPER 50

1. Simplify $\dfrac{2-\dfrac{1}{1+\frac{1}{3}}}{4+\dfrac{1}{2+\frac{3}{4}}}$.

2. A woman of mass 220 kg goes on a diet which claims that over 6 months she should lose 10% of her mass at the beginning of that time. What can she expect her mass to be 2 years later? Give your answer correct to the nearest kilogram.

3. If 1 m^3 of water has a mass of 1 t and mercury is 13.6 times as heavy as water, find the volume of 0.25 t of mercury in cubic metres, correct to three significant figures.

165

4. A photograph measuring 12 cm by 8 cm, which is surrounded by a border 3 cm wide, is increased so that its length becomes 27 cm. What does its width become if it is increased in the same ratio? Find the ratio in which the area is increased. If the *width* of the border is unchanged, find its new area?

5. The external dimensions of a lidless wooden box are: length 18.5 cm, breadth 12.8 cm, depth 9.6 cm. If the timber used to make the sides is 8 mm thick but the base is only 6 mm thick, calculate:
   (a) the internal volume of the box in cubic centimetres
   (b) the volume of wood used in its manufacture.